THIS THIEF, THIS MARAUDER WAS STORMING THE WALLS SHE HAD THOUGHT INVINCIBLE. . . .

As the assault on her mouth lessened in its determination to silence and became instead a sweet, practiced seduction of her senses—his arms loosening to hold rather than to constrict, his firm lips moving against the softness of her own with mesmerizing intensity—Cindy found that he was succeeding. A spark she had thought long dead and buried was igniting, and shock caused her to jerk away. She looked up at him with stunned violet eyes.

Slowly he lifted his head and smiled down at her. "There," he murmured. "Wasn't that a better way to make a scene than screaming?"

SWEET PERSUASION

Ginger Chambers

A CANDLELIGHT ECSTASY ROMANCE ™

Published by
Dell Publishing Co., Inc.
1 Dag Hammarskjold Plaza
New York, New York 10017

ISBN: 0-440-17524-0

Printed in the United States of America
First printing—December 1982

For Jean,
A friend from the past who remains one today,
even though my letters are spaced far apart. . . .

To Our Readers:

We have been delighted with your enthusiastic response to Candlelight Ecstasy Romances™, and we thank you for the interest you have shown in this exciting series.

In the upcoming months we will continue to present the distinctive sensuous love stories you have come to expect only from Ecstasy. We look forward to bringing you many more books from your favorite authors and also the very finest work from new authors of contemporary romantic fiction.

As always, we are striving to present the unique, absorbing love stories that you enjoy most—books that are more than ordinary romance.

Your suggestions and comments are always welcome. Please write to us at the address below.

Sincerely,

The Editors
Candlelight Romances
1 Dag Hammarskjold Plaza
New York, New York 10017

SWEET PERSUASION

CHAPTER ONE

The street corner was crowded with people waiting impatiently for the traffic light to change. Among them was a woman of slightly less than medium height and slender build, who had more reason for impatience than most. She stood stiffly, her shoulder bag hugged tightly to her side, her delicate features turned forward, her eyes attached to the Walk signal, willing it to hurry. But when that mechanism stubbornly seemed to take forever to light up, she was drawn to give a quick glance over her shoulder. What she saw made her stiffen even more and instantly evaporated what small amount of control she had left. Angrily she whirled to confront the man who was standing directly behind her.

"Look! I've told you once, and I'm not going to tell you again—if you don't stop following me, I'm going to call a policeman!"

The man was tall, several inches over six feet, undeniably attractive, with even, chiseled features and a lean masculine build that his dark business suit accentuated rather than hid. He smiled. It was a flash of white in sun-bronzed skin.

"And I've told you," he responded, his voice husky and deep and touched with more than a little assured amusement, "agree to come out with me, and I'll stop."

Cindy gritted her teeth, her thoughts none too generously centering on the authenticity of his parentage. "Go away! Get lost! Push *off!*" she all but shouted, frustration causing the level of her voice to rise. "Can't you hear what I'm saying?"

The man inclined his dark head and the sun caught and held the reddish-chestnut highlights in his hair. He seemed not the least affected by her vehemence. Instead, the appreciative humor in his warm brown eyes deepened. "Sure, I hear you. And so does half the city."

Cindy blinked at the unexpectedness of his reply, then a becoming pink flush rushed into her cheeks as she realized what he said was true. People were beginning to stare. With a furious sniff she pivoted forward, seething.

When the traffic light changed, she was the first off the curb, her small chin held high, indignation in every line of her slim body. But she had time to take only one step before a sudden gasp from the people remaining behind instantly combined with a deafening screech of tires.

Under normal circumstances Cindy was a cautious person. Living and working in a city the size of Houston had made her so. But this time she had been stupid; her mind had been filled with livid thoughts about the man who was following her, and she hadn't checked the traffic's flow. One time—one slip. She waited for the impact of heavy metal against her fragile flesh with only her mind screaming a protest.

But the expected strike never came. Instead, fingers that felt like a vise attached themselves to her arm and gave a powerful jerk, pulling her back onto the curb and up against the safety of whipcord muscles.

For a long moment Cindy lay against the hard warmth, shaken. She had never before come so close to being run down—and by a truck yet! The smooth cloud of her ebony hair rested on the jacket which smelled enticingly of a musky men's cologne. Then slowly her senses began to regain some semblance of normalcy and she started to push away, trembling, ready to give a heartfelt thanks. However, as she looked up, only one breathless word escaped her lips. It was a shocked "You!"

The well-remembered face was a little pale, but it was still maddeningly the same. "Yes, me," he concurred, a slow smile starting at the corners of his attractive mouth as humor at the irony of her situation began to chase away the shock of his concern. His arms remained firmly about her.

Immediately Cindy began a struggle to be free, but her strength proved useless against his determination. Finally, from between clenched teeth, she hissed furiously, "Let go of me!"

"No, I don't think so," he said mildly, shaking his head.

Cindy gave another twist, but it was to no avail. Incensed, she threatened, "I'll scream!" Using the old feminine standby seemed so weak . . . so inadequate—but at the moment it was all she could think of.

Her attempt at intimidation did not phase him in the least. "Go ahead," he prompted cheerfully.

Cindy's violet eyes began to darken with temper. Ever since she had first seen the man in the early afternoon, she had known he was going to be trouble. And her suspicion had been proved correct. He had walked into the office where she worked as a temporary secretary and, with an audacious wink, ignored her cautioning that her employer didn't want to be disturbed. He had then proceeded straight into the private office of one of Houston's top investment counselors. That he didn't come straight out again came as a surprise—as did the half-hour the extremely time-conscious Mr. Sawyer allowed to be taken from his busy schedule. But when both men appeared outside the door with Mr. Sawyer's normally serious face split into a beaming smile and his arm thrown jovially across the younger man's shoulders, Cindy began to understand. She understood even more when she was told that the visitor was a friend of the family's and was requested to secure a taxi for him. Mr. Sawyer had then retreated back into his office, expressing regret that he had an important appointment to prepare for and left Cindy to deal with the man.

The ensuing ten minutes were the longest Cindy had so far spent in her two weeks on that particular job. The man had behaved atrociously. He was so sure his physical appeal would hold sway with her, it was all she could do to keep her temper. He seemed not to accept that the word *no* was a valid expression in the English language. But since she was on her last day of work for Mr. Sawyer and valued her reputation as an efficient secretary, she was careful not to offend. It was hard though—something like walking a tightrope with climbing boots on. Then to find him waiting for her outside the building when she left for the day—and for him to follow her! It was too much!

Cindy took a deep breath in preparation for an ear-splitting scream. She was on her own time now. She didn't have to fear any repercussions. And he didn't believe she would do it. All together those were three very good reasons to wipe that laughing, confident expression from the handsome, arrogant face.

But just as the beginning of the scream formed in her throat, the man's head swooped down, and his lips strangled the sound before it had chance to be born. His arms crushed her to him with bruising strength.

During the course of her twenty-four years, Cindy had

long become accustomed to the fact that men wanted to kiss her—from the time she was ten and the first inkling of awareness of her appeal began to appear. Her mouth was soft and full, with more than a hint of sensuality in the curving line of her bottom lip. Her nose was small and straight and her violet eyes were wide-spaced and almond-shaped under delicate eyebrows that winged upward to disappear under wisps of coal-dark hair.

But, as well, over the course of those same years, Cindy had learned to be wary. She had learned the hard way that men and their desires brought pain as well as pleasure, and she had vowed never to again allow herself to be used. Toward that goal she had been successful. She was a new woman existing in a proud new age. She made her way through the world needing no one to complete her life. She dated; she liked to have a good time the same as the next person. But if a man ever tried to come too close, Cindy would immediately drop him. She had to be taken on her terms—and her terms only. She set the limits, drew the lines. . . .

Yet, here, now, this thief, this marauder, was storming the walls she had thought to be invincible, and she stiffened. Because as the assault on her mouth lessened in its determination to silence and became instead a sweet, practiced seduction of her senses—his arms loosening to hold rather than constrict, his firm lips moving against the softness of her own with mesmerizing intensity, their breath mingling with erotic intimacy—Cindy found that he was succeeding. A spark she had thought long dead and buried was igniting, and shock caused her to jerk her mouth away. She looked up at him with stunned violet eyes.

Slowly the man lifted his head and smiled down at her.

"There," he murmured, "wasn't that a better way to make a scene than screaming?"

Cindy's widened gaze swept upward to take in the cinnamon-brown eyes that were alive with devilment, the tanned skin stretched tautly across high cheekbones, the straight nose, firm jaw, and finally, again, the compelling mouth that had so recently touched her own. Then gradually she became aware of the people around them: Some were smiling, some were miffed at their display, and some were just curious. A whistle came from a car passing nearby.

Her cheeks were a fiery red as she wrenched herself out of the man's grasp and, almost before she had time to think, her hand snaked out in a purely instinctive reaction. When she heard the crack of her palm connecting with his flesh, she was almost as surprised as he.

Cindy looked blankly at her stinging hand and then at the man's cheek where the imprint of her fingers stood out in vivid relief. Inwardly she was appalled at her action, but on the outside she maintained her aggressive stance, or at least as much of it as she could muster. Her gaze met his unflinchingly.

A flare of momentary anger surged in the brown eyes but was soon buried under amused mockery as the man surveyed her small, defiant form.

"Next time I'll remember to duck," he mused with mocking whimsy.

"There won't be a next time," Cindy was quick to assure him, heavy frost on each word.

"You think not?"

He was so sure of himself, so confident. Cindy's backbone straightened. "I'm certain of it!"

"Why don't you call me Blake?" the man suggested

easily, not the least influenced by her continuing hostility. "That would be a start."

Cindy's hands came to perch angrily on both hips. "I'll call you something else in a minute if you don't leave me alone!" She was rapidly passing simple displeasure and well on her way to absolute fury. Gone was the unsettling disquiet of only a moment before. She was glad she had hit him! He deserved it! And if he so much as flexed a muscle toward her, she would do it again. Only this time she wouldn't stop with a slap!

The man had the nerve to chuckle, a pleasant sound that came from deep within his chest.

Cindy's hands clenched into tighter fists. She almost wished he would try to touch her again. If living with David for one year had taught her nothing else, it was the necessity of learning to defend herself. She was no longer a trusting girl on the verge of maturity. She was fully grown now, mentally as well as physically, and no man—no man—was ever going to take advantage of her again! Her attention was centered on the handsome face, oblivious to the crowd jostling by on the sidewalk, hurrying to their cars in the heat and humidity of a Houston summer afternoon, trying to gain a few seconds of time in the monumental traffic jam that would choke their efforts to drive home on the freeways that led out of the city.

"And after I go to the trouble of saving your life . . ." the man who called himself Blake murmured with an unholy gleam dancing in his eyes.

It disgusted Cindy to be reminded of that fact, but it was a fact she couldn't totally ignore. If he hadn't plucked her from the path of danger, she would probably be in an ambulance right this very minute on her way to a hospital emergency room in Lord knew what condition. But, then again, if he hadn't been pestering her, she wouldn't have stepped from the curb without looking! She opened her mouth to inform him of this but snapped it shut again, all in the space of a second. What good would it do? she wondered impatiently. She would just be wasting her breath. So far he hadn't listened to a word she said. What made her think this time would be different?

"Think what you like. I don't care," she returned tartly.

An eyebrow rose. "With not even a thank you—"

Cindy regressed into childhood and stamped her foot. "No!" she fumed.

The man shook his head, his thick brown hair full and curling slightly in its path to the collar of his light blue shirt. He sighed regretfully. "Somehow this isn't working out as I planned."

Cindy allowed a small triumphant smile to touch her lips. At last! He was finally getting the message! "No, I don't suppose it is," she agreed. "Now, if you'll excuse me . . ." She pointedly turned away. Her tone had been perfect: cool, precise, dismissing. She carefully checked the street before stepping away from the curb. People surged on either side of her, all hurrying mindlessly on a familiar path.

Cindy moved gracefully among them, her head held high, her slender figure complimented by a white linen skirt and matching jacket with a red silk blouse enhancing the glow of her unusually light-colored skin, congratulating herself on how well she had managed the situation—all except for that one little slip when he had kissed her. But that could be attributed to shock. It wasn't every day she was almost flattened by a truck!

She reached the next sidewalk and was starting to walk on when curiosity got the better of judgment and she paused to send a lightning glance over her shoulder. Afterward, she heartily wished she had not, because the now familiar athletic frame was still keeping pace with her. A few steps behind, it was true, but still very much present. Cindy glared at him then tried to pretend he wasn't there. In this she was a dismal failure. She quickened her pace, but it did no good. Finally, she stopped, her eyes glinting with purple heat and her small, rounded breasts heaving with agitation.

"What do I have to do?" she demanded, frowning fiercely. "Draw you a picture?"

Once again the man's reaction was that of amusement. "I've told you what you have to do—come out with me."

"You're crazy!" Cindy cried, his determination exasperating her.

"Only moderately," he replied, grinning.

Cindy could only gape at him. Unconsciously she began to shake her head, making the dark hair that fell from a center part move against her shoulders.

"I'll find a way," he warned, seeing her denial. "When I want something, I usually get it."

"Well, you won't get me!" she returned hotly, although a sense of unreality was beginning to overtake her. This wasn't really happening! She wasn't standing on a sidewalk of downtown Houston practically screeching at a man she had never met before this very afternoon!

The smile lines in his tanned cheeks deepened as he taunted softly, "We'll just have to see about that. Now, won't we?"

Cindy's blue eyes widened. The man was demented! He truly was! It was the only explanation she could think of for his actions. Only he didn't look insane. His gaze met hers steadily and contained both amusement and a fine resolve.

Cindy's heartbeat began to quicken. He meant what he said. He wanted to go out with her and he wasn't about to take no for an answer. What was she going to do? She had never been in a situation like this before! She looked about distractedly as if for inspiration. Then all at once an idea struck her, and she slowly allowed her eyes to rise to his.

"You want to go out with me," she stated needlessly, already knowing his answer.

The man nodded, his brown eyes narrowed on her delicate features.

"And if I agree, you'll leave me alone?"

Again the man nodded, but this time he added in a husky undertone that was filled with warm promise, "If you still want me to . . ."

Cindy did not allow herself any response to that seductive voice. Instead, she hurried on before she lost her nerve. "Then what's the matter with now?"

If the man was surprised, he didn't show it. "Nothing that I know of," he said, a smile flickering on his lips.

Cindy took a deep breath. "Will we go to dinner?"

"Are you hungry?"

"Yes."

"Then dinner it is."

Steely fingers once again took possession of her upper arm as he turned her about and began to walk back down the sidewalk against a thinner flow of people filing out of their offices.

"I've been away for a while," he remarked quietly as they retraced their earlier steps. "Is Cero's still open for business?"

"Er—yes. I think so." Cero's was an exclusive restaurant located in the downtown area that catered to the city's wealthier palates.

"Or would you rather go somewhere else?" He turned to glance at her profile.

Cindy thought furiously. "No, Cero's is fine," she replied. "But what about a reservation? Won't we need one?"

"We won't have any trouble," he assured her blandly.

At that Cindy said nothing, but she thought plenty. Confident, wasn't he? It must be hard to have such a small opinion of oneself and one's abilities!

The restaurant, which was their destination, was located on a side street, and its entrance was classically understated: raised gold lettering on a black background and two very large and heavy doors with a pair of green plants on either side.

Inside, the lighting was muted, with dark paneling and indoor plants everywhere. From what she could see, it was designed so that intimacy was the prime objective. A couple could be in the large room filled with people but never know it. It would suit her purpose perfectly.

Her companion consulted with the maître d' and was assured that of course a table would be found for them. Then he turned to her and inquired smoothly as he motioned toward a nearby bar, "Would you care for a drink? We have a few minutes to wait."

"Uh . . . yes. But if you don't mind, I'd like to freshen up a bit." She tried to say the words casually. "I must look a terrible mess." She attempted a light laugh, but it didn't come out with quite as much assurance as she wanted.

The cinnamon gaze went over her. "You look perfect to me, but go ahead if you want. I'll order the drinks. What would you like?"

"Oh, a white wine I think. I—" She looked about until she found the discreetly marked directions to the women's room. "I'll be right back."

She was lying. She knew it, but was beyond caring. All

she wanted to do was get away. She certainly had no intention of eating with him. She never had.

Cindy made her way slowly across the carpeted flooring, doing her best to fight down the nervous impulse to run. Several interested male glances followed her movement, but she was receptive to only one. The steady imprint of his eyes was like a brand on her back. It was with no small measure of relief that she was able to turn a corner and lean back weakly against the wall to wait, her heart pounding in her ears.

Soon two women walked by, deep in conversation. Cindy watched them until they disappeared through a door farther down the hall. She took a deep, steadying breath. Things couldn't be working better if she had had all day to plan and choreograph them. All she would have to do now was wait for the women to return, and then she could use them for cover, parting company with them as they neared the two heavy entrançe doors.

Cindy's nerves were stretched to the breaking point before the women finally reappeared. They were still talking as they neared her, but one of them paused long enough to lift an inquiring eyebrow in her direction. Cindy tried to smile in a friendly, casual fashion, but she could see by the woman's slight frown that the smile had been a little too strained. The second woman then cooperated by nudging her friend's arm and asking if what she had last said had been heard; Cindy was promptly dismissed as a curiosity.

As they walked past, she moved quickly behind them and slipped quietly into a position on their far side as if she belonged with them. When the trio entered the open area beside the bar, Cindy chanced a quick glance. But a cluster of people blocked her view and also his view of her. A thrill of pleased excitement rippled through her breast.

Better and better! It was as if the gods were watching over her escape! Quickly she turned toward the massive doors, a gleam of triumph in her violet eyes and a small smile of amusement curving her lips. She wondered how long he would wait before he came to look for her. Ten minutes? Fifteen? He would probably wonder if she were undertaking a complete restoration—from the feet up!

Cindy had to stifle a wicked chuckle. It would serve him right. He was so good-looking, women had probably been doing his will since the day he was born—his assurance gave vivid evidence to that fact—but she had no intention of joining their ranks. Not her. Not Cindy Thomas. He would have to mark her down in the category of the one who got away!

Some of the oppressive heat of the day had abated as Cindy stepped outside, and the contrast between the air-conditioned coolness of the restaurant and the temperature on the street as well as the brightness took a moment to adjust to. At six o'clock on a July afternoon the sun was still well above setting and Cindy had to shut her eyes against the stabbing glare that assaulted them.

Soon she became aware that someone was standing before her as if wanting to enter the restaurant. "Excuse me," she murmured, blinking like a small owl freshly disturbed from its sleep. "I'm sorry." She tried to move out of the way. Her eyes were adjusting, but it was a slow process.

The person moved with her. Finally Cindy moved again, thinking that somehow she must still be blocking the entryway.

"Haven't you forgotten something?" a husky voice asked, causing her to freeze.

The man! The horrible, insufferable man! Where had he

come from? He couldn't be here! He was still in the restaurant!

Cindy blinked up at him, at the darkly tanned face and hard brown eyes.

"Like maybe your drink?" he countered. "Or did you just lose your way?"

"I—I . . ." she stammered.

"I know, you just came out for a breath of fresh air." At that moment a bus pulling away from the curb a short distance down the street expelled a noxious cloud of exhaust and the fumes drifted down the sidewalk to surround them.

Cindy gulped and coughed. She couldn't think of anything to say. Her plan had been going so smoothly!

The hand that gripped her upper arm could not in any way be classified as anything but firm. "Come on," he directed. "You made a deal, and you're going to stick to it—even if it kills you."

The heavy door was thrust open and once again they entered the dimness of the restaurant. Cindy's vision, already abused, failed her, and she was led blindly through the room.

"Our table," Blake announced before almost forcing her into a chair.

Some of Cindy's paralysis began to thaw as he took his seat across from her.

"You can't do this!" she sputtered.

Blake leaned back in his chair, seemingly fully at his ease. "I already have."

Cindy gripped her purse. "I can leave if I want!"

Blake stared across at her, the hard masculine beauty of his face somewhat obscured by the indirect lighting. "You could," he agreed.

Now it was Cindy's turn to stare. She had never met

anyone like this before in her life. Obstinate, stubborn—those were only two adjectives that applied along with an entire list of many much more derogatory terms. And yet there was something about him. It was hard to deny, but she didn't have to like it.

At last Cindy sighed deeply and let her body relax. He was determined, if nothing else. And after the past two weeks, she was too tired to continue the argument. Let him buy her dinner if it made him happy. It wasn't as if she were agreeing to anything else. Afterward she could happily disappear and never have to see him again.

"All right. You win," she yielded wearily. "I'll stay."

"And you won't find it necessary to make any more trips to the ladies' room?"

Cindy allowed a small smile. "No."

The lines on either side of his mouth deepened. "Good. Because I don't mind leaving a bloody Mary, but I sure as hell mind leaving a good steak."

"I promise."

His eyes narrowed. "Your promises aren't worth a whole lot."

Cindy's back stiffened. "When I mean them, they are."

"And how is a person supposed to tell the ones you mean from the ones you don't?"

Small sparks of purple fire snapped in her eyes. "Look, if you're going to be unpleasant—"

He held up one long-fingered hand. "Don't say any more. And neither will I. Let's just have a nice quiet dinner. Get to know each other a little better and let everything else take care of itself. Do you agree?"

Cindy nodded briefly. She didn't want to know him any better, and she wasn't about to let him learn more of her, but to tell him so would only prolong the ordeal. And the quicker she could get this over with the better.

Surprisingly the meal was a success. When he wasn't actively trying to provoke her, he was quite charming. In fact, Cindy was barely aware of what was happening; all she knew was that as a dessert of cheesecake smothered in strawberries was placed before her, she was smiling at something he had said and was totally at ease—even to the point of making a teasing remark in return.

At that, she pulled herself up short. Good Lord, what had she done? Now he would think he had won her over and become even more of a pest!

The temperature at the table must have plunged a good twenty degrees as Cindy wiped the relaxed smile from her mouth and sat stiffly forward.

"I have to leave now," she announced.

Blake frowned. "Don't you want your dessert?"

"No, I . . . You eat it. I have to leave."

He studied her face thoughtfully. "All right. We'll go."

"You don't have to do that," she protested hurriedly, too hurriedly.

"No problem," he answered easily, a small motion of his hand signaling his readiness for the bill. The waiter came with satisfying promptness. When the necessary transference of cash was over, Blake stood to his full height and moved to help Cindy from her chair. He reached out to guide her toward the door, but Cindy pulled away. She didn't want him to touch her again. Instead, she walked gracefully ahead of him, her dark head high, her chin lifted—a much different picture from the woman who had stumbled unseeingly to the table.

The sun was setting when they once again entered the outside world, the rays casting a red-orange glow to the modern steel-and-glass buildings which lined the downtown streets.

Cindy permitted herself to turn to the man only when

she felt her emotions were fully under control. She still wasn't sure what had happened to her during the meal, but she was determined it was not going to happen again. She didn't like him. In fact, she couldn't stand him. And it was beyond everything she could understand as to how she could actually have been appearing to enjoy his company. Formally, she began: "Thank you for asking me to dinner—"

He didn't let her finish but interrupted with, "We must do it again sometime." His brown eyes were mocking. He knew she wasn't going to add that!

Cindy closed her mouth with a decided snap.

"Where's your car parked?" he asked. "Or do you ride the bus?"

Her feathers ruffled, Cindy answered shortly. "I'm more than capable of finding my car myself, thank you."

"Oh, I don't doubt that. I wouldn't put you past being able to do anything. You're quite a woman."

Cindy tipped her head slightly and demanded, "Are you making fun of me?"

Blake laughed. "Good God, no!"

She still looked at him suspiciously. She didn't trust him. Not an inch.

"Come on. Let me walk you to your car. It will be dark soon, and I don't think you should be on the streets alone."

Cindy expelled an exasperated breath. He always had an answer for everything! But in this case, he was right—and that fact served only to irritate her more.

"It's not far," she protested, trying one more time to be free of him.

"Lead the way." He refused to take the heavy-handed hint.

Cindy sent him a speaking look before swinging around

to march down the street. The man was like a leech! Once affixed, he was impossible to shake off. She covered the eight blocks to the car park as fast as was humanly possible, impatiently waiting at each traffic light that forced her to lose time.

Eventually she stopped beside a sporty gold Datsun 280-ZX and proclaimed tightly, "Okay. You've done your duty. I'm safe. Now you can leave."

The man looked at the car and back at her. "Do you have your keys?"

Cindy exploded. "Good grief! I don't know how I managed for twenty-four years without you!"

The man smiled down at her, the fine crinkles at the corners of his eyes deepening as his mouth drew up into a curving smile. "And I don't know how I existed for thirty-three without you either."

"I didn't mean . . ." She started to sputter indignantly but stopped when he continued as if she had not spoken.

"When we're old and gray and surrounded by our grandchildren, they're going to ask us how we met. We'll sure have something to tell them, won't we?"

Cindy stared at him stupidly, her mouth partially open. "You *are* crazy," she whispered at last. "I knew it all along, but I didn't truly believe it, not until now."

He took a step closer, forcing her back against the door of her car. Her breath caught somewhere in her throat.

"I told you I generally get what I want," he reminded her huskily. "And, lady, I want you."

Cindy was rendered completely mute. She watched spellbound as his hands came out to cup each shoulder, and his head lowered until his lips were touching her own. His mouth was warm and gentle, moving sensuously, coaxingly, trying to gain a response. But she was frozen to the spot; she could only stand there.

Slowly he drew away, a regretful expression marking his handsome features. He sighed and said almost as if to himself, "This is going to take longer than I thought. But, then, I guess if something is worth having, it's worth waiting for."

Unknown breathless seconds passed as Cindy continued to look at him, the panic shooting about her system belying her unmoving state. Then as he took a step back, yielding her space, Cindy forced herself to move and with trembling fingers fumbled in her purse for her keys. Once they were found, she inserted them into the lock and quickly slid into the bucket seat, slamming the door to behind her, intent on only one thing—getting away fast!

But as she started the engine and jammed the car into gear, Blake tapped on the closed window, causing her to throw him a startled look. Her heart contracted when he bent the length of his body to lean close.

"Come out with me tomorrow night, Cindy," he tempted softly, his words coming clearly through the glass that separated them.

A fine tremor ran down Cindy's spine; it was an occurrence she didn't welcome. Not since David had she felt such an intense, magnetic pull—and look what that had gotten her!

Wordlessly she wrenched her gaze away and pressed down hard on the accelerator, causing the back wheels to screech a protest on the dust-covered asphalt. When the car reached the street, she gave only a perfunctory check before whipping out into a break in the traffic.

But even then she found she was not completely safe from the man's fascination. Unwillingly her eyes were drawn back to give him one last look: he was standing where she had left him, tall and lean in his dark suit, with the glow of a streetlamp shining down on his thick chestnut hair. And he was watching her—his clear-cut features solemn, the smile which had been evident in his eyes and on his well-drawn mouth no longer there.

The driver of a van to the rear of Cindy's car gave an irritable blast of his horn, helping her to turn away. But the jarring note did nothing to alleviate the tumult of emotions that were churning in her midsection.

Her soft lips were tight as she quickly depressed the accelerator, the increasing speed putting distance between herself and the man who had so blatantly insinuated himself into her life . . . and what was more disturbing, into her consciousness.

CHAPTER TWO

Cindy spent the weekend acting, on the surface, as if nothing unusual had happened the previous Friday. Saturday she washed clothes and cleaned her pocket-sized apartment until it shined. Saturday night she went to a concert at the Music Hall. Church services, a game of tennis, and an impromptu party at one of her friend's houses took up Sunday and a good part of Sunday night.

It was only when she least expected it that an image of tanned, chiseled features would thrust itself into her mind and refused to be expelled. It was as if the man had cast some sort of spell on her! While she was applying wax to her linoleum kitchen floor; while calmly listening to a Beethoven symphony; while the minister was speaking; while waiting for a high lob to be smashed; while sipping a Coke, stretched comfortably on soft floor pillows listening to a friend chat about her work—the man would suddenly make his appearance. And she didn't seem able to stop thinking of him!

To say that Cindy was disgruntled was an understatement. For four years she had lived up to the vow to never again allow herself a deep response to a man. And she had been successful. For four years not one second of her time had been disturbed either while with, or away from, a man's company—until now. And she didn't like it, not any more than she liked the man. And especially when along with her memory of him came her reaction to his kisses. The first time she had been shocked; the second . . . well, she would rather not think about the second. It was more unsettling than the first. Her only relief came from the fact that she would never have to see him again.

But yet again a vision of warm brown eyes crinkled at the corners by a smile, inserted itself into her thoughts, and restlessly Cindy bent to flick the sheet down over the soft coverlet of her bed. It was late—well after one thirty, and tomorrow she would have to report early to the office, all bright and fresh for a new assignment. She had been stupid to stay out so late on a work night . . . and yet, somehow, tonight she had needed conversation.

Cindy crawled into her bed and relaxed with a long sigh at its comfort. She was tired. She could sleep for twenty-four hours straight. But as she lay still, waiting for blissful oblivion to overtake her, she found that her nerves were as jumpy as if they were the strings of a play harp set out in the middle of a kindergarten floor and children had been allowed to twang her unmercifully all day.

And that feeling could be centered on only one cause, one person: that stranger, that man, that Blake. He had done this to her! And all because he wouldn't let her be! Then or now. But what was happening at this moment was as much her fault as his. Surely she had more determination than to weakly allow herself to dwell on him.

Cindy stared at the mottled light that a streetlamp across the way from her apartment spread against her curtain. Look to the past. Always look to the past. And remember. Don't ever forget past mistakes—then it would be easier to turn her back and forget that this man existed.

With another sigh Cindy closed her eyes and willed herself to relax. She wouldn't think of him again.

* * *

Only circumstances didn't allow her fine resolution much time to gain strength. The first thing that happened Monday morning when she reported to the temporary agency to which she was contracted was that the young woman in charge looked at her curiously and informed her that she had received several calls on the answering service over the weekend. It was a man, she said, with a deep husky voice and who sounded about as sexy as any man possibly could. He had said his name was Blake.

In spite of her determination otherwise, a shaft of something mysteriously akin to both fear and excitement jumped through Cindy's body. But somehow she was able to control her startled emotions and was the picture of nonchalance as she asked, "What did he say?"

"He just left a number for you to call. Who is he, Cindy?" Marcy Stanley tipped her dark wiry head and peered at Cindy over the top of her glasses.

"A man . . . just a man."

"Some man from the sound of him."

Cindy gave a thin smile and changed the subject. "Got anything you think I might be interested in?"

Marcy took the hint and gave her a sheet of paper with the name of a private flying service listed. "I thought this might do for you. It's only for a week, but it's different."

Cindy let her eyes rest on the listing. A flying service. One delicate eyebrow rose.

"Shall I tell them you're on your way?" Marcy asked. "They need someone as soon as possible."

Cindy shrugged, her slender shoulders lifting the pale green material of her dress. "Sure." She checked the address and then the slim gold watch on her wrist. "Tell them I'll be there in about a half hour." The airport where the service was located was a small strip on the outskirts of the city and not far from the agency's office.

"I'll say forty-five and give you time to spare. You may need it with the traffic."

Cindy agreed and picked up her purse from the top of the desk where she had laid it. She was almost to the door when Marcy's voice halted her.

"Say . . . what about your calls? Don't you want the number the man left?"

Irritated with the increased beating of her heart, Cindy forced herself to shrug lightly.

"No, not particularly."

"But what if he calls again? What will I tell him?"

Cindy thought for a moment then broke into a lopsided smile. "Tell him I'm on safari and don't expect to be back for a year or two. Tell him Jacques Cousteau needed me urgently on the *Calypso.* Tell him anything. I don't care."

Marcy's chocolate eyes widened with understanding. "Anything but where you really are."

Cindy nodded. "Right." She turned to leave but was once again stopped by Marcy's words.

"If his voice is any indication of how he looks, do you mind if I try my hand? I'm asking, because I don't want to step on your toes."

Cindy dismissed her friend's concern with an airy wave of her hand. "Be my guest."

Marcy Stanley smiled. "Good. See you next week then."

Cindy waved and hurried to her car, all the while telling herself that it would be one of the best things that had ever happened to her if Marcy's dark good looks and engaging personality would capture Blake's attention.

The week at Miller Aviation seemed to fly by—no pun

intended, Cindy grinned wearily to herself as she placed the cover over the typewriter for the last time on Friday afternoon. Next week the regular secretary would return from her one-week honeymoon and be able to take up the reins of the business once again. If she could get her mind away from her new husband, poor innocent soul that she was. Right now she probably thought herself to have reached the pinnacle of earthly happiness. Little did she know how soon disillusion would tarnish her golden dreams. It hadn't taken Cindy very long. And the fifty-odd weeks that followed could have been born from a nightmare.

The hours of the weekend seemed eternal as they dragged by. Possibly because it was raining; possibly because of the depression that had descended on her Friday while remembering the bright hopes of the early weeks of her own marriage. Cindy didn't know. But a new restlessness took hold of her, and she was almost happy to see the beginning of another work week. Perhaps, with any luck, Marcy would have a really interesting job waiting for her. One that would take her mind away from, well, everything. Cindy refused to admit that as had happened the weekend before, more than once over the past two days her thoughts had turned to the man named Blake. And if the truth ever did assert itself, she salved her conscience by saying that the lapse was purely academic: She was only speculating if Marcy's diversionary tactics had worked—that was all. But a small stubborn section in her brain over which she had little control refused to believe that explanation and secretly wondered if in the morning, when she arrived at the office, she would be greeted with a stack of telephone memos containing Blake's imperative directives to return his calls.

Cindy was disgusted by her show of stupidity.

Marcy was on the telephone when Cindy entered the office early the next day. She looked up, waved her to a seat, then gave her attention back to the conversation. Cindy took a chair across the desk and couldn't seem to stop the strafing glance her gaze made as it searched the wooden surface for a collection of pink memo notes. There were none to be seen, and both relief and disappointment warred within her.

When at last Marcy finished her call, she took another moment to scribble a reminder on her calendar before looking up to say briskly, "Cindy! Just the person I wanted to see."

Cindy's lips flicked up into a knowing smile. "Oh?" she responded, the maverick side of her deciding that the memos had been so numerous Marcy must have been forced to tuck them away inside a drawer.

Marcy sat forward, her flat stomach pressed against the desk and her arms resting on its surface. "Yes. I have a job for you—a special one."

Cindy blinked. That wasn't exactly what she had been expecting to hear. Her ego took a well-deserved plunge, and her saner side was pleased. "A job?" she echoed.

Marcy broke into a teasing laugh. "Yes. Don't look so shocked. That *is* the business we're in. Stanley Temporaries, remember?"

A dusky flush traveled into Cindy's cheeks. "I remember. What is it?" She was being ridiculous! And it had to stop. With determination, Cindy regained her businesslike manner.

"A plum." Marcy flicked through several sheets of paper until she found the one she wanted. "Does the name Alan Michaels ring a bell with you?"

Cindy frowned. "No, should it?"

Marcy pursed her lips. "Think for a minute. If you had children, you'd know in an instant."

Cindy's frown deepened.

"Books," Marcy hinted further. "To name a few: *The Silver Tree, Small Time, The Duncan Trial,* and his latest—*Morgan's Mile.*"

Cindy's brow cleared instantly. "Oh! I remember that last one! You showed it to me a few weeks ago. You bought it for your nephew's birthday."

"Right," Marcy agreed.

"And Alan Michaels wrote it, didn't he?"

"Go to the head of the class!"

"But"—Cindy was still confused—"what does that have to do with me? I mean . . . I don't have children, or nieces or nephews either—"

"No . . ." Marcy drew out the word. "But you *are* a secretary."

Cindy frowned again. "I still don't understand."

Marcy raised her hands, interlaced her fingers, and supported her chin on them. "Alan Michaels is one of the best writers in his field, if not *the* best. He's won all sorts of awards—both national and international." She paused for effect. "And he's in the Houston area and wants a secretary. You!"

Cindy stared at her blankly. "Me?"

"You." Marcy sat back in her chair. "He comes from here, you know. Native son made good and all that. His home is in California now, but he's back in Texas for the next month or so to visit relatives—at least that's what his agent says." She glanced again at the letter. "He also says that Alan Michaels heard about our service from a friend and asked specifically for you. That he was adamant. Only you." Marcy glanced up, her gaze satisfied yet amused. "You must have made quite an impression on someone."

Cindy's eyes widened. "My goodness," she said weakly.

Marcy grinned outright. "I always knew you were the best secretary on my list—and this proves it. Now, listen, wait until you hear what he's willing to pay." She named a sum that effectively left Cindy speechless. "Quite a feather in our cap. And it couldn't have come at a time when we needed it more!"

Marcy did not have to explain what she meant. Cindy knew all too well. The influx of people to the Houston area had had an adverse affect on their business. At one time, and not too far in the past, a good secretary could name her own terms, but not anymore. People by the thousands were transplanting from the northern states to the South, with Houston the golden Mecca—and the competition for secretarial positions had become keener. Not to mention the temporary services. Stanley Temporaries wasn't about to go under yet—there was still plenty of work—but they couldn't afford to turn down a job like the one Alan Michaels was offering.

"When does he want me to start?" Cindy asked, her voice sounding breathless even to her own ears.

"Yesterday, like they all do," Marcy answered pertly. "Now, there is one catch . . . this is a live-in."

"A live-in! But I don't do live-ins!"

Marcy gave a long-suffering sigh. "Cindy, there are times when I could cheerfully strangle you. I know you have a rule against staying overnight at a client's house, but, and I repeat, but, this case is different. If Alan Michaels wanted you to work on the moon, I'd call NASA and reserve a space for you on the next shuttle!"

Cindy gave a wry smile and murmured, "Thanks." Then added, "Only the shuttle doesn't go to the moon."

Marcy gave another long-suffering sigh. She tapped the letter. "This expressly states that he wants you to live on the premises. It probably has something to do with artistic temperament."

"I can only hope . . . since I seem to be going to do it."

A playful smile tilted Marcy's lips. "What's the matter? Doesn't a little fooling around with a world-famous author appeal to you?" Then she burst out laughing at Cindy's appalled look. "I was only teasing. In all probability Alan Michaels is a little old man with bad eyes and afraid of his own shadow. But even if he isn't, I don't think there'll be any trouble. The man writes for children. He probably has to be extremely careful about his reputation. I know I've never heard anything particularly lurid about him."

Cindy retorted evenly, "Attila the Hun may not have had bad press in his day either."

Marcy began to chuckle. "Cindy, you're a treasure." Then she sobered and prompted, "Now go home, pack a bag, tell your friends you'll be out of pocket for the next couple of weeks." At Cindy's quickly indrawn breath she arched a brow that silenced her protest." And call me about five. I should have been able to contact his agent by then and have Alan Michaels's address. Okay?"

Cindy hesitated for several seconds, struggling with her conscience. Was it so very much for her to agree to this? It went against the decision she had made when first starting out in this business—close contact sometimes led to involvement . . . and involvement was the last thing she had wanted, and still didn't want! But Marcy had done so much for her—always looking out for interesting jobs, never questioning her personal life too closely even though they had been friends for the past four years. And for God's sake—the man *was* a children's writer. Cindy gave a short assenting nod and rose to her feet. At least one problem would be solved. By the time she returned in two weeks' time, maybe Blake would have stopped calling.

At that thought curiosity got the better of Cindy. "Er, Marcy? Did—ah—did that man ever call again?"

There! Now she felt like a complete idiot—and a hypocritical one at that.

Marcy glanced up from the note she had begun to write, her glasses slipping partway down her nose to the position they usually occupied. "What man?"

Cindy shrugged self-consciously, cursing both herself and Blake for her stupid behavior.

"You know, the one who called last week. The one—"

She got no further because Marcy interrupted. "The one with the deep, sexy voice?"

Cindy nodded shortly.

"Yes, he called. But I struck out. He was only interested in you." She twirled the pencil absently between her fingers. "It was all rather strange though, because when I told him you were out for the week on another assignment and wouldn't give him the number, he just seemed to give up. He never called back again, at any rate."

Once again Cindy was washed with two vastly different emotions: relief, because the man had given up, and dispirit, for the same reason. It seemed he was just like all the other men she had known in her life. Say one thing, do another. Pretend to be something, someone, then be another, and have all the constancy of a racehorse at stud.

When Cindy came out of her reverie, she found that Marcy was watching her with a quizzical look in her brown eyes. Hastily she shook herself and dredged up a satisfied, "Good. Personally, I believe he was more than a little insane."

Marcy breathed a heavy sigh. "Ah, for that kind of insanity!"

Cindy sent her friend a pitying look, then murmured a dry, "See you in two weeks," before letting herself out of the office.

The afternoon was spent in taking care of all the necessary details involved in being absent from her apartment for an extended period of time. A neighbor agreed to collect her mail, and another neighbor, a college student, greedily accepted the contents of her refrigerator. Her friends were contacted, dates cancelled, and luggage packed.

When all of this was done and there was still some time left, Cindy treated herself to a long soak in a tub filled with hot bubbly water and contemplated what Alan Michaels might really be like. Old, she agreed, remembering Marcy's attempt at a description. At least old enough to have grandchildren of his own who loved to have him gather them close and tell them stories. But his eyes would be sharp and lively, indicative of his vivid imagination. He would be a little on the chubby side, with a snub nose and white hair—a mane of white hair. And a beard! Suddenly Cindy began to giggle. It sounded as if she were describing Santa Claus! Then her giggling increased as her mind skipped on. Because if Alan Michaels were a Santa, what would she be? An elf? Somehow she had never seen herself filling that position! She liked variety; she wouldn't be working as a temporary if she didn't. But an elf?

At five o'clock Cindy made the call to Marcy and at five fifteen was in her Datsun, slowly carving a way through the heavy afternoon traffic leaving the city.

An hour and a half after that, civilization, as she knew it, was left far behind. She was proceeding down a narrow road of hard-packed sand which led deep into the piny woods of east Texas, and she was looking at nothing but trees. No houses, no stores, just trees, and she was having to fight an ever-increasing urge to turn back. Only her reluctance to explain that action to Marcy kept her going.

Cindy was a city girl. She enjoyed the noise of traffic, the sounds of construction, the bright lights—the polluted air! Possibly artistic temperament called for peace and quiet, but it wasn't for her. She felt restless in the country and the silence, except for her car's engine, seemed to be closing in on her.

Just when she had convinced herself that somehow she had received faulty directions and it would be with undented integrity that she could turn around and go back to the city, a small clearing appeared in the distance ahead and the road obligingly came to an end just as her directions indicated.

Cindy met that occurrence with a wry grimace. So much for the power of wishful thinking! Then she cut the engine and began to survey the scene before her.

What she saw was enough to delight any lover of nature at its primitive best: tall pine and oak trees rose high in the sky to compete with each other in the eternal race for sunshine and space; a greenish pond big enough to cover half a city block lay to one side of a rough rustic cabin. . . .

Cindy's horrified gaze fixed itself onto the quaint structure. Was it real? Quickly she blinked her eyes, hoping it would disappear. But it didn't, and Cindy groaned aloud in dismay. For there, sitting before her, proudly, stubbornly, was a real-life, honest-to-God, cut-down-the-trees-and-fill-in-the-cracks log cabin!

Slowly Cindy began to shake her head. No. It couldn't be. This had to be the wrong place. Either that or it was someone's idea of a joke. Surely Alan Michaels wouldn't be staying in a place such as this. He would want something much more comfortable—especially if he was a sweet grandfatherly type who probably had a heart condition as well.

Cindy took a deep breath and gripped the steering wheel tightly, feeling more than a little betrayed. She knew she couldn't expect the Taj Mahal out here in the middle of nowhere, but she had the right not to expect a hovel either. No wonder the man was willing to pay such a high fee! No one would work for him otherwise!

Reluctantly she released her grip and uncurled her length from behind the wheel, knowing that she could neither wish the place away nor magically turn it into a penthouse. And that, as a professional, she would have to at least try to work here. But Marcy was going to hear about this! And if ever she had another writer put in a request for a secretary, someone else would have to go. Because, she, Cindy Thomas, would absolutely refuse!

Cindy took a moment to smooth the lavender linen of her skirt down over her slender thighs and gave a last-minute touchup to the frilly collar of a matching lavender silk blouse. All the while she did this, she looked about with a cynical eye, not seeing anything to admire. Then she straightened her shoulders and began to march down the path strewn with fallen pine needles that led to the cabin's front door.

As she mounted the two steps onto the covered porch, her lips pressed firmly together. Well, at least the place looked sturdy. It could have been worse—like the building being ready to fall down around her ears. But if that had been the case, she would have had an excuse to leave. A good excuse. She felt like kicking a wall in the hope that it might crumble!

Cindy made a fist and rapped once imperatively on the heavy wooden door. When, after a few seconds passed and no one answered, she tried again, a flash of anger mingled with her already abused sense of indignation.

Where was he? He knew she was due to arrive. Marcy had told her that his agent said he was emphatic about her coming this evening. And now he wasn't here . . . or at least he wasn't answering his door. Cindy began to tap a foot furiously. She didn't care if he was a doddering old man, a Santa, or whatever. He should be here to greet her!

Then, from the back of the cabin, a series of deep reverberating barks shattered the stillness of the air, causing the fine hairs on the back of Cindy's neck to rise. She gave a start and jerked about—only to face one of the largest dogs she had ever seen in her life. He was light beige and looked as big as a horse and very obviously took offense at her presence here. His hair was ruffed, his eyes narrowed, and his huge white teeth were bared.

The only thing Cindy could think of at that moment was that he was going to eat her. That it would take only one champ from those huge jaws, and she would be in two separate pieces! She took a step backward, one hand rising to her throat and the other going out to the earlier much maligned door for support.

The dog didn't move. He just kept barking and snarling low in his throat.

Panic, pure unadulterated panic, caused Cindy's next action. If she had been thinking, she would never have done it; but at the time her thought processes seemed frozen, and instinct took over.

She began to run, tearing back down the path toward her car as fast as she could make her legs move. She didn't get far though; the dog began his chase the same second as she took her first step.

The snarling became like a roar, and hot canine breath was at her neck the instant she fell to the ground after being hit broadside by the large dog's front paws. Those same paws then rested like weights on her back, pressing her breasts flat against the ground. Cindy waited breathlessly, her cheek pressed to the dirt. There was little she could do to defend herself.

Suddenly, in the midst of it all, a masculine voice, harsh and urgent, called out a command, and the pressure on her back lessened. The roar changed to a questioning whine.

"Down boy! Stop it! Let her up!"

The dog finally removed his paws as the order came again. Cindy lay still, her eyes tightly shut, breath almost nonexistent in her body, her heart beating a thundering tattoo against her ribs. Soon strong hands were tugging at her shoulder, turning her. The first thing Cindy saw as she opened her eyes was the dog. He was sitting next to her, his yellow-brown eyes very intent, with the barest suggestion of a snarl still on his lips. Cindy swallowed tightly and stared back at him.

"Are you hurt?" The question was rough, unsteady with the emotion of the moment.

The numbness was leaving Cindy's body, and she made a movement with her hand toward her knees. They felt as if they were shredded, and stung when she touched them.

The man kneeling beside her uttered a harsh imprecation as he pulled her hand away.

Slowly Cindy turned her head, something about his voice cutting through the dazed mists in her brain. Her eyes widened as she gazed up at the familiar tanned features and cinnamon brown eyes.

"You," she breathed, shock mingling with disbelief.

As she spoke, some of the tension left the man's chiseled

features, and a slow smile deepened the fine lines at the corners of his eyes. "Helping you out of difficulties seems to be becoming a habit."

The light amusement in his husky, drawling voice had the effect of instantly clearing the muzziness from Cindy's thoughts. Her mouth clamped shut, and she struggled to sit up, pushing aside his offer of assistance with a muttered, "Thanks, but you've already done enough."

Blake sat back on his heels, allowing her space to move. "Grateful as ever, I see." A mischievous twinkle lit his eyes.

Cindy only glared at him.

The look did no good. If anything, his amusement increased. Then he suggested patronizingly, "You shouldn't have run. It's the worst thing you can do with a dog."

Her temper flashed. Her knees felt like fire and were covered in blood; her hose were destroyed; her new skirt was smeared with dirt and grime; and her blouse had a ruffle torn loose. And he had the nerve to lecture her?

Outrage vibrated in each word as she blazed, "Don't you dare try to tell me what to do! You don't own me!"

"I own the dog," he interjected calmly. "That gives me a little interest in the subject."

Cindy glanced at the dog in question. He was now sitting relaxed, his huge tongue hanging out one side of his mouth and a pleasantly interested expression on his hairy face. She turned back to the man and put every possible amount of revulsion she could into the question, "He's yours?"

Blake shrugged lightly. "All one hundred and fifty pounds of him."

"What is he? Part elephant?" she asked sweetly.

"Try mastiff."

Cindy chose another route. "He should be on a leash!"

"Why?"

"Because he's a menace!"

"Prince?" Blake seemed genuinely offended. "Prince isn't a menace unless you happen to be a squirrel or a rabbit."

"Of which I'm neither," she returned frigidly.

"Oh, I can see that." His warm brown eyes ran over her slender form, stopping for a moment on the shapeliness of her heaving breasts under her lavender blouse.

Cindy's hands clenched into fists, and she tried to rise to her feet. But her knees hurt so, it was impossible for her to do it alone. She had to suffer the aid of Blake's strong arm, although once she was up, she impatiently shook it off.

"We should put something on those knees," he advised.

"They're fine," Cindy grated obstinately.

A shadow of anger settled on his brow. "Like hell they are!"

Blake didn't wait for her to form another protest. Instead, he leaned forward as if to scoop her up into his arms.

Cindy stopped that foolish idea at once. "I can walk!" she hissed.

Slowly Blake straightened and, with his eyes narrowed, stepped away and motioned for her to proceed.

Without a word, Cindy took a step. Then another. Each one was agony, but she wasn't going to give in. She wasn't going to let him know how much pain she was in. She wouldn't give him the satisfaction.

By the time she remounted the porch steps, fine beads of perspiration were evident above her upper lip. But doggedly she made her way to one of the rough wooden roof supports, there to wait for the door to be opened.

Blake brushed past her, his back stiff.

Cindy's eyes followed, dully noting that today instead of the expensively tailored suit he was dressed much more casually in jeans and a well-worn denim shirt. And that, as she had suspected, not an ounce of spare flesh marred the masculine perfection of his body: wide hard-muscled shoulders narrowed gradually to a slim waist, taut hips and long supple legs were lovingly hugged by the faded material of his jeans.

She blinked when he turned to catch her stare and an embarrassed heat entered her cheeks as an amused eyebrow rose in mocking inquiry.

Cindy lifted her chin and tossed her head, making the midnight length of her hair swish against her shoulders. In fine determination she took another step. She didn't care what he thought! She could look if she wanted! Men didn't hesitate to. And certainly he had not bothered to restrain himself since the first moment they met!

All at once Cindy seemed to freeze. Good God! What was she doing? And what on *earth* was this man doing here? This was supposed to be Alan Michaels's cabin!

Blake held her wide-eyed gaze, his left hand remaining on the partially opened door, his body taut. Then he relaxed and a half smile of inevitability curved his lips.

"What a way to begin," he murmured.

A frown was darkening Cindy's brow. "I don't understand . . ." she began, her deep blue eyes fixed on his face.

"The dog. I hadn't meant for you to be hurt."

Cindy absorbed this. No, he probably hadn't . . . but what *had* he intended? "I still don't understand. I'm supposed to meet a man here—Alan Michaels—to work for him," she added hurriedly when she saw the flash of amusement enter his brown eyes.

"Go on."

Cindy glared at him. "*So*—what are *you* doing here?"

"I live here."

The simple answer infuriated her.

"But you can't! This is Alan Michaels's house . . . er, cabin."

"And if I were to tell you that *I* am Alan Michaels?"

"I wouldn't believe you!"

"Why not?" The easy humor in that question disconcerted her.

"Because . . . because . . . Alan Michaels is a writer . . . a children's writer—"

"And I can't be a children's writer?"

"No! Yes! Oh, I don't know!" Cindy ran a distracted hand over her hair.

Blake watched her harried movement and leaned back against the door frame, a smile of sardonic humor creasing his cheeks.

"Is it so hard to believe? When you pictured a man who writes for children, what did you see? A grandfatherly type? Somebody totally sexless? A eunuch? Because from first-hand experience I can tell you that I'm not and that also, whether you like it or not, I *am* Alan Michaels."

CHAPTER THREE

The gruffly spoken words seemed to echo in Cindy's brain. Him! Alan Michaels! It was impossible! Alan Michaels was a Santa! A nice old man with a heart condition, not this vibrantly masculine, totally virile, breathtakingly handsome specimen of manhood standing before her!

"No, you can't be!" she denied, her voice sounding faint.

The laughter in his warm brown eyes deepened. "My publisher believes me. My agent believes me. And so does the government when it comes time to pay taxes. Could you ask for better references?"

For the longest time Cindy seemed capable of only two things: standing and staring. Then a fine trembling seized her slender form, and her violet eyes began to glow with molten fury.

"*You tricked me!*" she accused.

"Only a little," he agreed.

"You made me come all this way for nothing! Nothing!"

"Oh, I wouldn't say that."

"*I would!* Why you . . . you . . ." she spluttered to a stop, the appropriate words no longer available.

Blake moved away from the door, his long easy strides making short work of the small porch. "Come on. We can discuss what I am later. Right now, let's get those knees taken care of."

Cindy drew a sharp breath. "If you think . . . I'll let you lay . . . one hand on me . . ." Her voice was shaking from the depth of her emotion.

"I'll lay more than one in a minute." His mouth clamped shut, the muscles on either side of his lean jaw rigid.

Hard brown eyes clashed with purple ones in a monumental battle of wills. The man, arrogant, confident, accustomed to having his own way. The woman, outraged, independent, determined to win.

The fire fight could have gone on for days but for the dun-colored mastiff that ambled into a position behind Cindy's back and woofed once questioningly. The sound was nothing like his earlier barking, but it rumbled in his great body like distant thunder. And coming as it did into the thick silence between the two humans, it caused Cindy to jump as if she had been shot and take an involuntary step forward. She couldn't prevent the cry of pain that escaped her lips. After standing for so long, arguing, the blood had dried on her knees and her movement had torn at them.

Blake wasted no more time on words. He half-dragged, half-carried Cindy into the cabin. Soon she found herself sitting on an old overstuffed sofa with him kneeling on a rug before her.

He brushed aside her protesting hand as she tried to prevent him from lifting the hem of her skirt well up onto her thighs.

"I've seen a woman's legs before," he growled.

"I'm sure you have," Cindy responded with tart sweetness. Tears of discomfort were forming in her eyes, but she was determined to keep them at bay.

Blake glanced up, saw the moisture, then looked down again. "If I leave you here for a few seconds, will you promise not to run away?"

"No." The answer was short, obstinate.

The creases in his cheeks deepened and a flash of white teeth showed when he smiled. "Well," he drawled easily, "since you're slowed to a hobble, I think I'll chance it." But before leaving he turned to the dog, who had followed them inside and was now sitting in a waiting position at the end of the sofa. "Watch her, boy," he directed.

The dog's ears perked up, and he turned large yellowish eyes onto Cindy.

Cindy met his gaze. She heard the amused laughter Blake gave but didn't see him leave. She was busy watching the dog, who was busy watching her. Their mistrust was mutual.

After a few short minutes, Blake came back into the room carrying a large bowl filled with water, a cloth, and a first-aid kit. He knelt in front of Cindy once again then ordered, "Okay, boy, relax." And with a teasing glance at Cindy. "You too."

Cindy transferred her fixed gaze to Blake. She started to say something suitably cutting, but at that precise moment, a warm wet cloth was placed against one knee, and she had all she could do to gulp back a reaction to the sting.

With infinite gentleness, Blake washed away the dirt and blood and applied a soothing coat of antiseptic cream. This done, he rummaged in the white plastic box and from the bottom produced two large gauze pads. These he applied over the wounds. When he was finished, he leaned back against his heels.

"There, almost as good as new. But if I were you, I'd

rest up for a day or two—at least as much as you can. Let those knees start to heal. They're cut pretty badly."

"I might. Thank you," Cindy answered coolly, her back having straightened as soon as he sat away from his work.

An uneasy silence descended and Cindy, rather than look at him, examined her surroundings with some curiosity. She had never been inside a cabin like this before and was surprised at the warmth and comfort she found.

The room they were in was large and the walls were covered with rich pine paneling. In addition to the sofa, there were two chairs, a table, and a lamp. Against one wall stood a bookcase which was filled to capacity, and above the large stone fireplace was hung a beautiful oil painting of a forest scene. Two doorways led out of the room in addition to the one they had entered from outside. Each exited into a different area. Vaguely, Cindy found herself wondering what the other rooms were like. But at that she pulled herself up short. There was no use wondering; she wasn't going to be here long enough to find out.

Blake must have read her mind, because he slowly got to his feet, his long length unwinding with athletic grace. He looked down on her from his full height and murmured, "I'll let you have tomorrow off. Then you can start work. I think that would be only fair since it was my dog that caused the problem."

Those words had a galvanizing effect on Cindy. She took a deep breath and exploded, "You've got to be kidding! You don't seriously expect me to stay here, do you?"

Blake gazed at her calmly and folded his arms across his chest, the sleeves of his shirt rolled up to reveal muscular tanned forearms. "We have an agreement," he stated.

"We don't!" Cindy corrected. "My agreement was to work for Alan Michaels."

"And I am Alan Michaels."

"So you've said. But I haven't seen any proof. Anyone can talk about publishers and agents."

Blake looked at her for several long seconds before turning to walk to the bookcase. Once there, he plucked a paperback from its place on the shelf and came back to hand it to her.

Cindy stared down at the glossy cover. It was an exact replica of the one Marcy had bought for her nephew a few weeks before: *Morgan's Mile,* with the author's name, Alan Michaels, beneath.

"Turn it over," she was directed.

Gingerly Cindy did as she was bid. And on the back was something she had not seen on Marcy's book—a photograph. It was of the man standing across from her.

Cindy swallowed and looked up.

"All right. You are who you say you are but you still tricked me! You knew I wouldn't work for you if I knew who you were!"

That slightly garbled sentence seemed to make perfect sense to Blake. "You didn't return my calls so I knew the only way I'd be able to see you again was to hire you." He took the book out of her hands and returned it to the shelf.

"So you admit you lied!"

Blake shook his dark head. "I didn't lie."

Cindy glared at him with impotent fury. "But you certainly didn't tell the truth!"

"I did. I am Alan Michaels. And I do need secretarial help."

Cindy clenched her hands into fists and hit her thighs in one quick motion while she let out an outraged squeak.

Blake started to laugh. "Face it, Cindy. You're trapped. If you refuse to work for me, it won't look very good for your agency—or for yourself."

At that moment Cindy didn't want to be bothered by

thoughts of consequences. "You think you're so smart!" she all but spat. "Did it ever occur to you that I might not care?"

He shrugged. "Sure. But I dismissed the thought as unworthy of you."

Cindy's eyes sparkled with dangerous fires. "You think you know me so well?"

"I believe so. Through the years I've learned to be a fairly good judge of character. Are you going to prove me wrong?"

Cindy would have given almost anything to wipe that smug look from his face, but after a gigantic wrestle with her conscience, she found that she couldn't do it. She was a professional. And professionals didn't let a little thing like intense dislike stand in the way of doing their jobs. And it was also true what he said about it not looking good for the agency. How would she even begin to explain the situation to Marcy?

"No," she finally answered. "I won't. But something has to be understood . . . right now . . . right at the beginning. If you so much as touch me . . . with one finger . . . I'll disappear so fast you'll wonder what happened!" That was one thing Marcy would understand. Nothing made her angrier than for one of her employees to be harassed sexually on a job.

Amusement pulled at his well-cut mouth. "Just one finger?"

Cindy seethed. "*One finger!*"

Blake's firm lips twitched into a smile. "That should be easy. All right, I'll agree."

Cindy watched him suspiciously for another moment then nodded her head shortly. The deal was made. She was probably letting herself in for all kinds of trouble, but it was a chance she was going to have to take. As Marcy had said, it wasn't every day a person the caliber of Alan Michaels contacted their agency . . . and if he happened to be a little light in the attic area, well, she could deal with that. Just so long as he didn't try anything funny—touch her or kiss her—or overstep in any way the bounds that separated their professional relationship.

Her pride took a decided jolt though when after asking if she would like to see the room she would be using and receiving a cool nod of agreement, Blake swooped and collected her into his arms before she could utter a sound.

"All in the line of duty," he explained, very tongue-in-cheek. "You shouldn't be walking."

Cindy started to protest but was soon stopped by the necessity to hang on. Blake strode across the floor and through one of the open doorways as if unmindful of the burden he bore. Cindy, clinging to his neck, wondered if all the jostling was truly necessary. The unholy light in his eyes as he deposited her weight on a quilt-covered bed told her that it was not.

"Thank you," she snapped, looking daggers at him.

"You're welcome," he replied, the daggers not penetrating the thick hide of his skin.

Cindy pointedly started to straighten her lavender blouse, fuming to herself all the while and hoping that he would take the hint and leave. She glanced up when she was done only to find that he was still there.

"Well?" she demanded.

"I was wondering if you were hungry."

"Hungry?" she repeated stupidly.

"You know, as in food?"

Cindy's cheeks took on an annoyed color. "No!" she answered ungraciously.

"Is that no, you don't know about food? Or no, you're not hungry?"

Small perfectly formed teeth ground together. "Are you trying to make me angry?"

"I don't have to try very hard, do I?" He was failing in his attempt to smother a broad grin. "Do you think that might be trying to tell you something?"

"I don't have the slightest idea what you're talking about!" Cindy turned until she didn't have to look at him any longer.

"Oh, I think you do—or you will, if you let yourself think about it."

Cindy continued to stare at the wall, at a painting reminiscent to the forest scene she had noticed earlier in the other room. She relaxed only when she heard the sound of his footsteps recede as he slowly walked away. Then she flopped back against the soft pillows and wondered what she had ever done to deserve finding herself in such a mess.

Not five minutes passed before Blake was back in the room, causing Cindy to jerk up into a sitting position. A light flush covered her cheeks at being caught in so vulnerable a position.

"What do you want this time?" she demanded irritably.

A gleam of irritation flashed in his brown eyes but was quickly subdued as he answered calmly, "I thought I'd bring these in. But if you don't want them—" He lifted her set of matching luggage.

"Oh!" Cindy was somewhat ashamed of her previous rudeness. Normally she was a pleasant enough person. It was only in this man's presence that the worst side of her nature seemed to spew forth. Ill at ease, she replied, "Er—thank you. Yes, yes, I do want them."

Blake dropped the cases onto the many-colored rag rug which covered most of the room's wooden flooring. "I also wanted to tell you that the bathroom is the first door to the left after you leave this room. And that if you want, I'll take you there now."

The flush that had never truly left Cindy's cheeks deepened. "No. I can walk. My knees barely hurt at all now."

"A miracle cure," he murmured.

Cindy's chin jutted stubbornly. "You might say that."

"Then in that case, you can start work tomorrow. God knows I can use the help."

"That suits me perfectly, Mr. . . ." She tilted her head to one side. "Just what do I call you anyway? Is Michaels your last name, or is it a fake too?"

Blake looked pained. "Why do I get the feeling that you think more than my name is fake?" When she didn't reply, he continued, "My full name is Blake Alan Michaels. I dropped the Blake in my writing as a matter of privacy—only my friends call me that. And as for what you should call me? I seem to remember asking you to call me Blake."

"But I'm not one of your friends. I just work for you," she reminded him smugly.

His comeback was immediate. "Then I'm ordering you to call me Blake."

Cindy glared at his chiseled features and cursed him mentally. "Oh, all right . . . Blake!" she returned icily.

A devilish light played in his brown eyes. "Try it again. Only this time add a little warmth. *That* could have rivaled a blue norther in freezing ability."

"I'll see what I can do," Cindy gritted, determined that hell could freeze over before she would say his name again!

Blake smiled wryly. "Practice will make it easier," he prompted.

When Cindy remained stubbornly silent, he sighed resignedly and left the room.

It was a shock, but Cindy slept deeply that night. One minute she was planning all the different Machiavellian tortures she could inflict on one Blake Alan Michaels and the next she was prizing her eyelids open and wiggling her nose to the delicious aroma of frying bacon as it drifted into the room from the other side of the closed door. At almost the same instant she made the discovery that she was ravenously hungry. All she had eaten before leaving her apartment in Houston was a small bowl of soup and a salad. Now the vast hollow area that was her midsection was demanding something more, responding with wholehearted enthusiasm to the tantalizing smell that was filling the room.

Cindy threw back the light cover and bounced from the bed, her thoughts centered on only one thing: food. It took approximately two steps before the pain from her badly scraped knees jerked her to a stop. She had forgotten all about them; but they, perversely, had not forgotten her nor had they healed sufficiently to allow her freedom of movement.

As the pain became bearable she limped over to her suitcase and slipped on her short robe. Then armed with fresh underwear she slowly made her way to the door. He had told her last night that the bathroom was just down the hall. . . .

Cindy wrapped the lapels of her robe more closely over her small breasts and removed the vanity chair from its restraining position under the knob. In the light of day her precaution of the preceding night seemed more than a little ridiculous; but she knew that when night came around once again, she would just as carefully replace the chair. An unsullied virgin she was not but then she didn't trust this man any further than she could throw him and was determined not to be snuck up upon while she slept.

After a glance of surveillance Cindy headed for the bathroom. The cool water felt wonderful as she washed up—she only wished she could take time for a full shower—but her distrust of the man and the impatient rumbling of her stomach left her no option.

Taking another cautious look she was back in her room extracting a light summery dress from her suitcase and sending up a silent prayer of thanks that the soft pink material was uncrushable. Last night she had been in no frame of mind to unpack.

She took another few minutes to apply some lipstick and mascara and to pass a comb through her dark hair; she didn't want to appear the way she felt inside—as if she were a starving gypsy child who would wolf down whatever was placed before her.

Once she was satisfied that she looked cool and collected, she again opened the door and let her nose lead her to the kitchen. It was the second doorway leading out of the main room. There she found Blake humming to himself as he tipped fluffy yellow mounds of egg onto two plates. His glance at her was perfunctory.

"Hope you like your eggs scrambled. Do you take juice or coffee or both?"

His back was to her as he put the skillet into the sink and ran water into it. This morning he was again wearing jeans, only this time they were tan and the shirt he wore was a striped cotton pullover that faithfully clung to each muscle of his strong back. Cindy couldn't prevent the way her eyes ran appreciatively over his long form.

He glanced back over his shoulder, an eyebrow lifted in inquiry, and Cindy started guiltily. This was the second time in as many days that he had caught her staring. She would have to stop before she gave him more ideas than he already had!

When she made no reply, a glimmer of a smile pulled at Blake's lips, and he turned to lean back against the counter, the heel of each palm resting on its surface, his eyes taunting her.

"Now, don't tell me you're still not hungry," he jeered.

At that moment, because of his superior, mocking tone, Cindy would have loved to inform him coolly that she wanted only a cup of black coffee, but her watering mouth would not allow her to speak the words. Instead, she retorted, "No, I won't tell you that, because it would be a lie . . . and *I* don't lie."

"And neither did I," he shot back, instantly understanding her parry.

"Which is the only reason I'm still here."

Cindy took a seat at the small wooden table which boasted only two chairs and deftly flicked the paper napkin that was resting beside her eating utensils onto her lap. Out of the corner of her eye she saw Blake push away from the counter and pick up the two deliciously laden plates. He placed one into position before her and the other in front of the empty chair.

"You never answered." He remained standing. "What would you like to drink?"

"Coffee, please." Cindy's eyes fastened hungrily onto the eggs and three slices of crisply fried bacon. Her stomach gave a famished growl, and it was all she could do not to pounce on the meal before her.

A white mug filled with steaming black coffee was placed beside her hand. "Milk's in the refrigerator if you want it," Blake murmured before taking his place across from her.

"Thank you."

Cindy picked up her fork, unable to wait any longer. The smell was driving her crazy! But before she could place the loaded instrument into her mouth, Blake's husky voice drawled, "You're being very polite all of a sudden."

Cindy lowered the fork. Damn him!

"I'm always polite to my employers," she answered with false sweetness.

"I guess that's what I'm counting on."

"Which? My employee status . . . or my manners. I guarantee that where you're concerned, they go hand-in-hand."

Blake started to shake his dark head. "You're slipping," he warned.

"In what way?" Cindy's patience was wearing thin.

"Your manners."

"Well, maybe I'm one of those people who don't like to hold conversations before breakfast!" She jabbed her fork once again into the mound of eggs.

"That's not the impression you gave a minute ago."

"I don't care what I did a minute ago!"

"Your eyes are too bright, too alive—"

The eyes he was speaking of were crackling with impatience. "Will you please stop talking about me!"

"But I like to talk about you—and to you. Why else would I go to all the trouble of getting you here?"

Cindy abandoned her fork altogether. "You want me to work for you, remember? Or was that just another . . . deception. I'll use that word, since you seem to be allergic to *lie.*"

"There's work to be done—plenty of it. But I also counted on a little time for play—a chance for us to get to know each other."

Cindy grunted. It was inelegant, but it was what she did. "Did you ever stop to think that maybe I don't *want* to get to know you?"

"You're fighting me, Cindy." His brown eyes were filled with amusement.

"You're damn right I am. I also think you're crazy!"

"Only about you."

Cindy picked up her fork and amassed another bite of food. It didn't matter that her once ravenous appetite had now disappeared. "I'm going to eat," she announced.

"Go ahead. All I want to do is make you happy."

"Then leave me alone!"

He shook his head regretfully. "I can't do that."

Violet eyes struck sparks. "Then I'll leave. I told you I would if you touched me."

"I haven't touched you . . . yet! But I think there's something important you're forgetting."

Cindy's delicately winged eyebrows rushed together in a frown at those mysterious words.

"I don't—" she began.

"Eat," he interrupted. "Your eggs are getting cold."

Almost automatically Cindy obeyed, her thoughts jumping from one idea to the next, trying to puzzle together what he could possibly be talking about.

The rest of the meal passed in silence. It wasn't until they were drinking the last of their coffee that the quiet was broken by a loud, rumbling bark from outside the kitchen door which was a rear exit to the cabin.

Cindy remarked sardonically, "Your friend is calling you."

"He's hungry. He didn't get fed before I let him out this morning and growing puppies need a lot of food."

Cindy batted her eyelashes. "Puppy? And I thought you never lied."

"I never said that I didn't *ever* lie. I'm not a saint. But Prince is a puppy. He won't be a year old for another month. He's still a baby."

Cindy twitched in her chair. "Some baby. And he's calling you again."

"You want to let him in?"

"No, thank you. I'm going to my room to unpack."

"What about helping me with the dishes?"

Cindy glanced at the plates, utensils, and mugs that had been dirtied, then let her violet eyes rise slowly to his as she confided solemnly, "Now that's the trouble with some men. They just don't seem to understand that a temporary secretary is just that—a secretary. You wouldn't believe the problems our agency has had in the past. Men get the strangest ideas into their heads." There! Let him take that any way he wished!

Blake received the double-sided message loudly and clearly. "Touché!" he murmured softly.

"I thought you'd see it my way," she returned.

She started to rise from her chair, but Blake's next question halted her. "Does it happen often?"

"What? You mean being asked to do housework?"

An annoyed frown settled on his brow. "Stop trying to act innocent. You know what I mean."

Cindy reneged. "I've had my share of male employers forget the exact reason they hired me but I've always been able to handle it . . . and them."

"But you don't like it."

"No. Would you?"

A slow sensuous smile creased his lean cheeks. "I might."

Cindy did a slow burn. A typical male reaction! But should she have expected anything different, considering the source?

"A man can't be blamed for doing what comes naturally," he went on to say.

"Naturally for what? A rabbit?" she demanded. Really, the man was just too much!

Blake began to laugh. "What does a rabbit have to do with what we're talking about?"

Cindy was not amused. "Everything! There is such a thing as control!"

"A *rabbit* with control?"

At his continued obstinate misunderstanding of what she was trying to say, Cindy exploded, "*No!* Oh, I knew this would never work out! I knew it last night!"

"If you would just explain—"

"I'm leaving! I'm going to my room; I'm getting my things—and I'm going to leave!"

"I can't persuade you to stay?"

"No!"

Blake sat forward, leaned his forearms on the table, and shook his head sadly. "I wish you wouldn't."

"Well, that's just too bad! You should have thought of that before you—"

"Before I what?"

Cindy glared at him. "Never mind. I don't want to waste any more breath talking to you."

She struggled to her feet, fighting to hide the grimace the action produced, then turned to walk stiffly from the room.

It was as she crossed the threshold of the doorway that she thought she heard the sound of a soft, deeply amused chuckle come from the man who had remained behind. But she couldn't be sure; the sound had been very quiet. And she wasn't about to turn to find out. If Blake Michaels thought something about the situation was funny, then let him. As for herself, all she wanted to do was escape! And the sooner, the better!

CHAPTER FOUR

Cindy fumed all the way to her room, whipping up her anger, not letting herself delve into the dark area of her mind which taunted her with the fact that she was grasping at straws for any excuse to leave. Because if she did, she might not like what she found. And that disturbed her almost as much as the possibility of what she might discover. If only Alan Michaels had been any other man!

Cindy threw the few articles she had used that night into one of her cases, uncaring of what might be crushed. Then she reached for her purse and began to dig into it for her keys.

One minute later she was upending the purse's contents onto the quilt. Pocketbook, lipstick, comb, a collection of Kleenexes—one with a piece of gum wrapped securely inside that she had forgotten to throw away—everything but her keys. They were not there!

A little desperately Cindy searched through the contents once again, and, after having no better luck, explored the lining of her purse, hoping that they had somehow become caught in a tear. But it was no use.

Slowly she sank down on the edge of the bed, going over in her mind the last time she had seen them. All at once she remembered. She had left them in the car! Last evening she had been so surprised, not to mention disgruntled, at finding that the house she was expected to work in was nothing more than a cabin, she had left them dangling in the ignition.

Cindy hurriedly gathered her possessions back into her purse, and, pulling the strap onto her shoulder, collected her suitcases before struggling to the door. Her knees were aching, but they would just have to ache. She didn't have time to give in to them. Later, when she was back in her apartment, they would be pampered. But not now.

After trudging her way through the house and onto the porch, Cindy continued as quickly as she was able down the pathway to her car. Once there, she pushed her luggage onto the rear seat and slipped behind the steering wheel, her heart beating rapidly and her eyes searching for any sign of Blake. So far, he had not come after her—a fact that confused her somewhat, especially when he had been so adamant that she stay. But, in that, she supposed she should count herself as lucky—at least she wouldn't have to resort to a scuffle in order to leave.

With practiced efficiency Cindy reached toward the ignition and began the motion that would start the car. However her fingers encountered nothing but air.

For a moment Cindy remained where she was, stunned, unable to believe what had occurred. Then slowly the reality of the situation became clear to her, and she began a frantic search of the area around her, looking everywhere—on the floormats, in the glove compartment, along the crevices in between the gear shift box and the two bucket seats, which would have been a perfect place for keys to take refuge. But it was no use. They were gone.

Several ineffectual seconds passed as Cindy grappled with a helpless feeling of inadequacy. Where could they be? She had driven here, so she had proof that they had been with her at some time yesterday afternoon. She forced herself to think. On seeing the cabin, she had turned off the ignition, then she had gotten out. With dawning comprehension, Cindy's eyes followed the line the pathway made as it led to the cabin.

Blake! It was Blake! He was the one responsible! Now she knew why he had not tried to stop her, why he had laughed. *He* had her keys—and he had taken them last night when he brought the luggage into her room. No wonder he had been so assured, so . . . so . . . This was all a game to him!

A deep black anger began to build in Cindy's breast as both frustration and fury fed the fire, and she started to tremble. It was a fine quaking that had nothing to do with fear. How dare he do this to her! How dare he think he could play this kind of trick! He seemed to be of the opinion that he could force her to stay. Well, he couldn't! She wouldn't let him. A memory of his soft laughter spurred her temper on.

With her midnight hair flying around her face from her hurried, furious movements, Cindy climbed from the car and slammed the door behind her with force. The action felt good—she only wished it had been on his head!

When she stormed back into the kitchen, she found that Blake was standing at the end of the counter bending to pet the huge dog whose nose was firmly entrenched in a large plastic food bowl. Cindy's flashing eyes took in the dog's presence, but she was so angry, she didn't care. She marched to within two inches of the pair and flared angrily, "All right! Where are they?"

Blake looked up, a blank expression on his handsome face. "Where are what?" he questioned.

Cindy had to physically restrain herself from hitting him. "My keys, damn you!"

"Your keys?" Blake repeated the words as if he had never heard of such objects before.

"Yes," Cindy hissed. "You know, those little metal things you took from my car!"

Blake straightened, and the dog took time to momentarily look away from his food, his suspicious yellow-brown eyes leveling on her.

"What makes you think I took them?" Blake finally asked.

"Because you're the only other person here!"

A slow smile moved over his mouth, which had the effect of making Cindy's heart skip a beat even in the white heat of her fury.

"Are you sure you haven't lost them?" he suggested easily.

Cindy recovered herself. Damn it! Why this man? Why her? Why now?

"Yes!"

Blake leaned back against the counter and crossed his arms, his cinnamon-shaded eyes watching her closely under long dark lashes. He took several seconds before speaking.

"Well, then I guess maybe I must have."

"What?" Cindy's patience at his obscure answer was nonexistent.

"I said," he repeated softly, "that I suppose maybe I must be the one who lost them."

"Lost . . ." Cindy echoed, not believing what her ears were hearing.

"I do seem to remember having them last night—"

Cindy's anger exploded. "So find them! And find them now!"

Blake was unmoved by her anger. "How can I find them, when I've just told you that they're lost?"

"Conveniently lost! You've got them somewhere, Mr. Blake Alan Michaels. And you know damn well where they are!"

Another slow smile crossed his attractive lips. "I didn't think you'd believe that," he murmured.

Cindy's eyes widened. "So you admit it!"

He shrugged his muscular shoulders. "I suppose I'll have to."

Cindy didn't know what to say next. He seemed to be running her in circles! Finally she clung to the one word that jumped into her mind. "But that's kidnapping!"

He dismissed the word with ease. "Call it what you like. I prefer to think that I'm protecting my business interests. I hired you for a job, and now you're trying to leave without fulfilling your part of the bargain."

"We have no bargain!" Cindy was livid.

"Agreement then."

"We have no agreement!"

"Your agency does."

"To hell with my agency! And to hell with you!"

Blake had the affrontery to laugh outright, which caused Cindy to launch herself at him, no longer in control of her anger. She wanted to do something, anything, to ruffle that calm, mocking confidence of his. He had been a nemesis to her from the beginning—a curse almost.

But somehow her plan did not work out as she had wanted. Instead of being unprepared for her attack, Blake seemed ready for it. He neatly sidestepped as she thrust her body forward and wound his long steellike arms about her, pinning her against his chest and effectively stopping with his strength any thrashing movement she might make.

Cindy's face was flushed with her efforts when finally she became still, but hatred shot tellingly from her violet eyes. His body was hard, warm, and the musky scent he used emphasized his blatant form of masculinity. Cindy noted these things just as she noted the dog was now standing stiffly beside her, a low, warning growl coming deeply from within his throat.

Blake looked down into her heated face. "You might as well accept it, Cindy. I'm not going to let you go."

Cindy's voice shook slightly as she breathed. "I'll report you to the police!"

"That will have to wait until you can find a telephone. Fortunately, or unfortunately, whichever way you want to look at it, there isn't one here."

"I'll file charges!" Her voice was still shaking from the depth of her anger. "You'll be put so far under the jail the authorities will forget that you're there!"

Blake pursed his lips wryly. "That will be your prerogative—when I decide to let you leave."

Cindy bit back the next angry words that tried to spring from her tongue. It was no use. He seemed to think he had an answer for everything. But she wasn't defeated. No, not yet!

Blake released his grip somewhat. "Everything will be much simpler if you just relax. As I've told you before, I just want us to have a chance to get to know each other better. And I believe, if you let yourself, you'll admit that wouldn't be such a terrible thing."

Cindy clamped her mouth shut and glared at him.

Blake looked down at her stubborn, obstinate face, at the small chin which was filled with determination, at the normally softly drawn, seductive lips which were being held in a tight line, and he released his hold entirely.

Cindy jerked away from him, shaken more than she liked to admit by her reaction to the closeness of his lithe body. Not since David . . . or rather when she had first met David . . .

Cindy tossed her head defiantly, her loose dark hair dancing in reflexive action.

Her movement caused the dog to stiffen even more, and Blake, noticing this, gave a sharp command for him to sit. Cindy took in the exchange, watching sourly as the large dog immediately obeyed.

Did Blake Michaels think he could command everyone and everything as easily as he did his dog? Did he think everyone would react as meekly to his every wish? Did being a writer and playing God with his characters make him think that people were merely puppets to be moved at his whim?

Cindy's chin tipped upward and her slender shoulders straightened. Well, if he did, he had met his match in her. She was just as determined as he—and as stubborn. Their only difference was that their goals were situated at two different poles: his for her to stay, and hers to get away.

Blake's low-pitched, husky voice broke into her thoughts, and she roused herself in time to hear him say, "It won't be so bad. And if it will make you happier, I'll only keep you here for the specified two weeks."

At that magnanimous concession the flash of molten sapphire which discharged from Cindy's eyes would have pierced even an elephant's skin, but Blake seemed to barely notice.

"I have a manuscript to be typed from a handwritten draft," he continued, "and some minor revisions—"

Cindy stopped his flow of words by telling him exactly and succinctly just what he could do with his blessed manuscript and revisions.

Blake chuckled appreciatively. "I don't believe that's anatomically possible, Cindy." Then he went on as if he had not been interrupted. ". . . and some minor revisions to another manuscript that has a deadline the end of this month."

Cindy almost choked. She began to sputter. She could remember no time in her life when she had been quite so incensed by someone who was so close to being a stranger.

"If you think I'm going to type calmly while you're keeping me here against my will, then—then you're softer in the head than I thought! I will *not* work for you! *I won't type a single word!* You can do it yourself if you want it done!"

"But I can't type." He shrugged one shoulder, the teasing light still warm in his eyes.

"Then that's just too bad!"

"Maybe you'll change your mind."

"Don't hold your breath!"

Blake once again leaned back against the counter, a gleam of challenge in his brown gaze. "That will have to be added to everything else we're going to have to see about, won't it?"

A delicate rose flush stained Cindy's cheeks. "*We* won't see about anything."

"Oh?"

"No—because if I'm going to be held hostage, then I'm going to act like one! If this cabin is to be my jail, I'm going to my cell . . . and I'm not coming out again until you regain some of your sense."

"Two weeks is a long time. All by yourself, with no one to talk to."

"If the only choice I have is to talk to you, I'd sooner cut out my tongue."

"A rather drastic action."

Cindy's small nose tilted. "But appropriate."

Blake's sense of humor, never far away, broke through

the bonds he had been trying to set on it, and he began to laugh softly. "Woman, you have got to be the most stubborn person I have ever met."

"And you're one of the more obnoxious!"

Blake's brown eyes sparkled with mischief. "We make a good pair then—both so alike."

Cindy clenched her fists, her nails digging into the soft flesh of her palms, the word *murder* uppermost in her mind. But somehow she forced herself to regain control. It would accomplish nothing if she continued to argue with him. No, the best thing she could do was to be alone—to think, to plan.

After several long seconds had stretched between them, Cindy turned abruptly away, not deeming to make a reply.

But a lack of words seemed never to be a failing of Blake's—maybe that came with being a writer. He called after her, "Think about it, Cindy. Think how easy it would be if you'd just stop fighting yourself and admit what we both know to be true. How much easier it would be on both of us. Attraction is a powerful thing—one of the most powerful forces in the world. Stronger even than a person's will."

Childishly Cindy clapped her hands over her ears, her heart thumping like a pump gone wild. She didn't want to listen to him. She wouldn't listen! She had been through it all before.

She hurried to her room and jerked the door shut as if it were the last bastion of safety between her and some kind of devouring monster.

As Blake had predicted, the following minutes and hours seemed to drag by, but rather than fume at the absurdity of her situation, Cindy used the time wisely by deciding on the best method to use for her escape. Numerous plans came to mind, from bashing Blake over the head with a lamp—which she didn't think he would just stand there and let her do—to prying up the floorboards of her tightly shuttered room and slipping away through the open space beneath the cabin—an act she had neither the strength nor tools to accomplish—to pretending to change her mind and agree to start work for him, then one day when his guard was down, just disappear quietly out the front door, except that she didn't want to be around him that long.

The plan she finally settled on had everything: it was the most practical, the one most promising of success, and, as well, it was immediate. She would wait until nightfall, sneak out of the cabin after she was sure Blake was asleep, then she would walk all the way back to Houston if need be. And if for some reason she was unable to leave this night, she would leave the next! Or the next! Or the next! Her will, which Blake had spoken of in so cavalier a fashion, was set in obstinate determination. She would gain her freedom, and she would gain it with very little delay.

Midway through the day a knocking sounded on her door, causing Cindy to almost start out of her skin. Everything had been so quiet in the cabin up until then. In fact, several times she had been tempted to check to see if her captor was still there. But good judgment had prevailed, and it now had been proven correct.

"Cindy, it's Blake," the unmistakably husky voice informed her.

Cindy drew her knees up to her chin, hugging them with her arms. She was sitting in the middle of the bed, where she had been for some time. There was very little to do in the room.

"I didn't think it was Prince," she snapped back, wanting to sting him, her mood not improved by being startled.

There was a pause, and she wondered if she had finally succeeded in disconcerting him. But, when he spoke, his words were tinged with humor.

"No, I don't suppose you did. I'm going to make lunch. Would you like some?"

Cindy remained silent.

"Cindy?"

"I'm here."

"Steak, salad, rolls . . ."

Cindy's stomach rumbled. Quickly she subdued it and retorted acidly, "My, you are quite the little homebody."

Blake laughed out loud. "You could say that."

Again silence stretched between them.

After several seconds Blake finally spoke. "Am I to take it that you're trying to tell me you don't want anything?"

"You take it right," Cindy answered sweetly.

Blake sighed. "Okay, but if you change your mind . . ."

"I won't," came her reply, each musical sing-song note laced with saccharine venom.

"You may," he responded in kind. Then he added tauntingly and with dual reference, "Hunger can make a person do strange things."

At that Cindy reached for a pillow and crushed it tightly against her knees. But when that attempt at releasing her pent-up frustration failed, she regressed into infanthood and stuck out her tongue as far as she could possibly make it extend. She found the experience strangely satisfying. Then she had to slap a hand over her mouth to keep from giggling at the picture she must have made. Who would believe that she was twenty-four? Sitting perched on the bed, a pillow reduced to a mangled ball on her lap, and her tongue thrust out in a secret gesture of defiance toward the man outside her door. Four would be more accurate.

To her relief, the cause of her problem shifted position and soon the soft sounds of his footfalls could be heard as he retreated down the hall.

Cindy let out a deep breath of relief.

The next half-hour was tortured by the scent of the steak Blake was broiling for his lunch as it drifted through the cracks around the door. Drat the man! He knew exactly what he was doing! And he knew later as well. Because for his evening meal the unmistakable scent of highly seasoned chili came to assault her.

For a woman of her slenderness and size, Cindy had always had an enormous appetite. She could eat what she wanted and not gain an ounce much to the disgust of her plumper friends. It had something to do with her metabolism, she supposed. But as well as being an advantage under normal circumstances, it had its darker side as well. It was tremendously hard for her to skip a meal. And being forced to do so twice in one day, she blamed squarely on Blake Michaels. Another black mark to add to his ledger—particularly when this last time he hadn't even asked if she wanted to participate!

The following hours proved to be the hardest. Night had arrived. She could tell by the general darkening of what little outside light penetrated the room and by the lessening of the frequency of the gentle hum of the cabin's air-conditioning system. The exterior world was cooling off as well as preparing for rest and Cindy could hardly contain her mounting tension. She lay on the bed, staring up at the darkening void where the ceiling had once been, and forced herself to wait, deigning not to switch on the lamp so that Blake would think that she was asleep.

The wait seemed interminable. But finally her hard-won patience was rewarded with the sound of his approach. Every muscle in Cindy's body tightened as his footsteps paused at her door. He stood there for a moment, as if in indecision, then breathless seconds later he moved away, and soon Cindy heard a door close a short distance down the hall.

Like a conspirator in a dime-store novel, she felt the tension sag from her body, only to be replaced by another sort—the kind that demanded action. Yet, still, she made herself wait. She could ruin everything if she was in too much of a hurry. Blake had to be asleep. Otherwise . . .

No, she wouldn't think about otherwise. She forced herself to play memory games in her mind—multiplication tables, her parts in the junior and senior play at her high school. She concentrated on anything but her desire to hurry.

When at last the cabin had been still for what seemed to be hours and in all probability was barely thirty minutes, Cindy pushed her weight from the bed and soundlessly walked across the rug. At the door she paused, a nervous film of perspiration dampening her palms. Carefully she slid the door open a narrow crack.

Nothing was moving anywhere but a soft light coming from the living room spread its muted rays into the hall. It caused Cindy to blink and jerk her head back behind the door. Could Blake still be up? Was that the cause for the light? Had her ears played a trick on her before when she thought she heard him moving into his room?

With her heart beating strongly, Cindy debated what to do. Long seconds passed and her straining ears heard no sound. So after taking a deep breath, she took a chance and peered once again out from behind the cover of the door. The scene that greeted her was the same: silence and the soft glow of a lamp.

Cindy's shoulders straightened, a contingency plan quickly forming as a solution. If it were Blake and he was still awake, she could make the standard excuse that she couldn't sleep and wanted a glass of warm milk. She might have to take some of his amused barbs, but that would be better than waiting and later finding out that the light was left on as nothing more than a giant night light! And if that were the case, her passage from the cabin would be made all that much easier. At least then she wouldn't have to worry about tripping over something and alerting him to her attempt at escape.

With her breath barely lifting her breast, Cindy let herself out of her room and glided stealthily down the hall. Then just as she had seen in hundreds of television shows, she flattened herself against the wall beside the living room door frame and slowly inched her head forward until she could see into the room.

The relief that flooded through her was almost enervating. Just as she had thought—Blake wasn't there! The lamp, on its lowest setting, was only giving direction to the night. If she had waited for it to be switched off, she would have wasted the time for nothing!

However, she still knew she would have to be cautious. She wasn't home free yet! Guided by the light, she began a careful exit of the cabin.

She attained the halfway mark in the living room before noticing the great beige clump lying asleep on a small rug in front of the fireplace. Prince! In all her planning she had completely forgotten about the dog. Immediately Cindy stopped in her tracks and cursed herself for her stupidity. All it would take would be one creaking floorboard . . .

To her extreme dismay, even as she thought those words, the dog, who had been sleeping soundly when she stopped, seemed to have sensed her presence and began to rouse. His ears twitched, his head moved, and slowly his eyes came open. A film seemed to cover them, but as Cindy watched with fascinated absorption, the film soon receded and the massive head raised, his eyes focusing directly onto her frozen form.

Prince wasn't deceived for a second by her rendition of a statue. Only instead of jumping up and giving off a series of loud barks that could be guaranteed to disturb even the soundest of sleepers, the dog only looked at her, a sleepy expression covering his face, and slowly began a weak thumping with his tail. Then, puppy that he was, his head fell back to the comfort of the rug and nestled in between his front paws. Then with a long sigh of canine contentment, he once again closed his eyes.

At that particular moment Cindy didn't know whether to laugh or cry. Instead she moved stiltedly to the rough wooden door, afraid that at any second the dog might change his mind. With economy of movement she released the wooden bar from its locking position and, within the second, was outside.

The first thing she became aware of as she recovered her scattered wits was the darkness. When night fell here, it fell. She had never been in such darkness before. In the city there was always light coming from some artificial source. But here! It was nearly impossible to see!

Her courage faltered at the thought of striking out in the blackness alone, but she quickly shored it up. If it was a choice between the devil she knew and the devil that might be out there, she would take the devil out there!

Cindy groped her way across the porch then stopped, glancing up to see that the sky was lighter in comparison to the earth below, but overcast, the brightness of the full moon hidden as if behind a thick veil. Yet it did give off some light, and as she waited for her eyes to become more accustomed to the night, she was able to pick out the narrow roadway which cut a path through the dark mass of trees on either side.

Swallowing tightly, Cindy slowly began to move toward the road, passing her useless car with barely a thought, except for wishing she had learned the trick of hot-wiring it. She then turned, and to the accompaniment of tree frogs chirping in volleys from one high perch to the next, and with the trees themselves closing in suffocatingly near, proceeded down the firm-packed sand road.

To say that Cindy was out of her environment was a colossal understatement. She had never felt so vulnerable to nature, so naked and alone. She felt completely at the mercy of elements she had never encountered before. But as she continued walking, putting distance between herself and the cabin, she slowly came to the realization that she was winning in the battle to contain her fear and that at the end of this experience, when she was once again safely back in her apartment in Houston, she would emerge a stronger person. She would have confronted the enemy that was within herself and defeated it.

Just as she was congratulating herself on her newfound reserve of strength, a rustling sound came from the undergrowth directly ahead of her, and before she had time to take a breath, an animal of some kind—she couldn't identify what—scuttled out into the middle of the roadway.

Automatically Cindy took another step, abject terror not yet having gone from her brain to her feet. Then she faltered, coming to an instant halt.

The animal stopped as well. It was small with bright,

beady eyes that glowed in the partial light. It looked Cindy straight in the eye.

Cindy could only stare back, her fear intensifying. The closest she could ever remember having been to a wild animal before was at the zoo—and then it had been behind bars!

Suddenly the animal began to move, its direction unclear to Cindy's eyes. She didn't know whether it was continuing on its way across the road or launching an attack. With a little yelp she jumped backward and began to hop from one foot to the other.

Her excited movement decided the case, because her panic confused the animal, and in an answering panic it began the charge she had feared.

Cindy observed the hurried advance with wide, frightened eyes. Then, with another terrified yelp, she whirled and began to race away, uncaring if her flying feet were retracing her earlier escape route from the cabin.

With a pounding heart and breath which came out in shaky gasps, Cindy tore down the road, wanting only to find sanctuary. She had covered only a short distance when she careened full tilt into something which had the solidness of a wall. Only this structure was alive and had arms that came out to gather her against a familiar, warm closeness.

At that moment Cindy didn't care if she had been in the process of escaping from Blake—that somehow he had learned of her attempted bid for freedom and followed. All she cared about was that he was there, holding her, protecting her. An uncontrollable tremor shuddered through her slender body, and Blake increased the pressure of his arms, a hand coming up to press her head against the smooth nakedness of his chest.

"What is it? What happened?" his husky tones inquired.

Cindy shook her head, her fingers clinging uninhibitedly to the warmth of his skin and the soft sprinkling of body hair on his chest.

"Did something frighten you?"

If Cindy had been at her best, she would have ripped that inane question apart; but as it was, she only nodded convulsively, yes.

"What happened?"

Cindy gave a low moan. "It chased me—"

"It?"

Cindy nodded jerkily. This was not how she had planned the night to go, but shaken as she was, it mattered little.

"How big was it?"

"N-not big."

She felt Blake's chest begin to move with silent laughter. She hated herself for giving him the opportunity to ridicule her, but was incapable of doing anything to stop.

"It was probably a possum or a raccoon. The woods are full of them. At worst it was a skunk."

A shudder passed over Cindy once again. Show her a spider or a lizard and she was fine. But a wild animal . . . with teeth . . .

Blake continued. "None of them would hurt you, not unless you tried to hurt them first."

Being Texas-born and bred, even if it was in the city, Cindy knew this, but it was one thing to talk about the inhabitants of the far-off sparsely populated areas, and another thing entirely to face said animal practically nose-to-nose! Unable to control her reaction, Cindy burrowed closer to Blake's reassuring warmth.

Blake's only response was to chuckle softly and tighten his hold.

How long they remained standing in the middle of the roadway, closely entwined, Cindy had no idea. She was aware only of the loud chirping of frogs and of Blake holding her close, and of his amusement at her display of needless fear.

Then, gradually, a subtle change began to permeate the force field of air around them and a lightning spark of awareness began to grow with each second that passed—an awareness which was as old as time itself, yet still as strong as the moment it was first discovered.

With tantalizing slowness Blake's fingers curled tighter into the softness of Cindy's hair, at the same time directing her face upward.

Like a doll being positioned by the master's hand, Cindy allowed the movement. Then she raised her eyes and saw the closeness of Blake's shadowy features. The sight filled her vision and she stared up at him, unable to move her gaze away, awash in a feeling she had not experienced for a long, long time.

The first touch of Blake's firm lips was a soft, tentative exploration, and Cindy knew that she should pull away. That she should stop him. Stop herself. But as her body began to burn with tingling sparks of reawakening life, she was incapable of doing either.

CHAPTER FIVE

At a later point Cindy might try to convince herself that Blake had taken advantage of her, had capitalized on her fright, had made her respond to him while in a state less than her optimum best. But deny it as she may, at that moment she knew exactly what was happening. And she welcomed it.

There, in the night, in the middle of a forest, with a man she adamantly detested, a rush of desire surged through her and she couldn't keep herself from responding.

It was something like being caught in an avalanche. Resist as you may, the force of nature's fury carried you onward, and you were helpless to prevent the outcome.

For so many years she had denied herself, denied the passionate nature that still existed buried deep within her. And now, like a bottled explosive, feeling returned with overwhelming force.

The pressure of Blake's kiss increased as he sensed her melting compliance, his arms drawing her closer.

A burning heat began to radiate from Cindy's body, crying out for—demanding—an answering warmth. Her breasts seemed to be on fire as they flattened against Blake's hard chest, the smoothness of his bare skin alien yet attractive to her curved fingertips.

With growing need Blake's hands moved over her back,

caressing the narrow line of her waist and the gentle swell of her hips, where they stopped to mold her to him, making her wholly aware of his fully aroused need.

Cindy gave a small groan as a remembered ache began to grow—a white-hot urgency that demanded fulfillment.

Blake dragged his mouth away to run kisses down along the side of her neck, his breathing rasping heavily, the searing fire that was throbbing in her veins echoed by the passion in his.

As her face tipped farther upward, Cindy closed her eyes against the overcast sky, absorbed only in sensation.

Blake's lips moved to her ear and he softly murmured her name, making a thrust of shivering emotion shoot through her. She raised her arms to encircle his neck, her fingers seeking and finding his thick chestnut hair.

When he moved once again to claim her lips, Cindy was the one to draw his head closer. And she was the one who made the first move toward even greater intimacy as she ran the tip of her tongue along Blake's well-curved lips, enjoying the soft, sensuous thrill that had been absent from her life for so long. Then, with increasing boldness, she thrust her probing tongue even farther, invading the moistness of his mouth and teasing the tip of his tongue.

Blake's response to this action was a wild flurry of desire that broke through the bonds of what little restraint he had left.

He jerked her even closer against him, and one hand came up to massage the rounded curve of one breast.

Caught up in the excitement she was experiencing, Cindy didn't object when, with sudden decision, Blake swept her from the ground, an arm beneath her knees. Not one word of protest passed her lips as he began the long walk back to the cabin.

Cindy didn't care! She wanted exactly the same as he!

If this were an avalanche, she was riding it—and she would ride it to the end. If there were danger, she would face that when the time came. Right now only one thing mattered.

Only one thing.

When they reentered the cabin, Blake didn't pause to do more than close the door. He ignored Prince's sleepy wag of his tail and half-hearted effort to rise, and proceeded directly into his bedroom, his brown eyes glittering hotly with tautly suppressed desire.

Cindy met that look, and returned it with one of her own. Each was caught in the trap of mutual need.

As Blake lay her on the surface of the quilt which covered his bed, Cindy supported herself on one arm as she rested on her side. She retained his gaze. She couldn't look away. She watched as, instead of stretching out beside her, he sank onto the edge of the bed.

"You're a beautiful woman, Cindy," he observed huskily. "But you'll be even more beautiful without this." He flicked a finger along the soft material of her pink dress and she trembled uncontrollably as the back zipper was smoothly released. Blake trailed his fingers along the silky expanse of skin, stopping only at the hindrance of her bra. Skillfully he released it as well. Then, with infinite gentleness, he pulled the superfluous material from its place on her arms, exposing her perfectly formed small breasts.

For a moment Cindy wanted to grasp the dress back against her. David had always complained that her breasts were too flat—that she was near to being a boy. But Blake didn't look dissatisfied. He stayed her instinctive movement.

"Beautiful," he murmured then followed that action with his lips.

As his mouth moved from one tingling mound to the

next, Cindy slowly lay back against the mattress. Blake went with her, lowering his length onto the bed, his long, muscular thighs running parallel to her own.

Delicious ripples of sensation fanned the fire that was burning brightly in Cindy's soul as Blake's tongue played with her hardened nipples. Unknowingly, as she arched upward she cried out his name.

Blake lifted his head and a satisfied smile pulled at the corners of his mouth. Then he turned his attention to the ball of material about her waist. To an impatient Cindy, it seemed to take forever for him to finish removing her clothing—his hand running appreciatively over the smooth curve of her hip, along the firm length of her thigh, teasing the sensitive area behind her knee, until at last her feet were free . . .

When he was done, his cinnamon eyes ran over her, and with definite purpose he allowed his hand to slide back up the silky texture of the skin of her inner thigh.

Again an uncontrollable shudder passed over Cindy, and she uttered a low-pitched moan.

It was madness! Total complete madness. She wanted him like she had wanted no man ever before in her life! And she was determined to end this exquisite torture. She had to have him—and it had to be now!

With a jackknifing movement, Cindy sat up, Blake's hand having moved to her flat stomach. She pushed it impatiently away.

When he drew back surprised, she smiled at him and leaned over to kiss the smooth bronze skin of his shoulder.

Blake relaxed . . . and waited for what she would do next.

Since jeans were his only outer clothing, Cindy was presented with little problem.

She, too, had had experience undressing a man—although David had never thought much of letting her do it. To him, the sexual act itself was all that mattered. What came before and after had to be finished with as quickly as possible.

But Blake didn't seem to mind. Cindy got to her knees and with tempting leisureliness unsnapped and unzipped the faded blue cloth.

Then, as if almost unable to help himself, Blake did the rest. It was only a matter of seconds before he was back beside her, pushing her down onto the bed, and wrapping one lean leg over her own.

"I've got to have you, Cindy," he rasped, his husky tones thick with desire.

Instead of answering him with words, she told him with her hands and lips and soft breath that she wanted him as much as he seemed to want her. She ran her lips across his chest, trailing a fiery path to his smooth abdomen. Her hands sought to learn every inch of him, caressing the heavy muscles of his shoulders and back and his sturdy, muscular thighs. He was beautiful to her and she thrilled at his husky moans of pleasure, the way he repeated her name in a voice strained with mounting passion. Finally his hands stilled her own and he raised her, wrapping his arms around her once more, enclosing her in his warmth.

When she looked up at his face, her violet eyes glowed with anticipatory pleasure and a hunger that could no longer be denied. Blake's lovemaking was wonderfully exciting, yet full of tenderness and sensitivity. It felt so right to be in his arms, so natural to ache for complete and utter closeness with him.

He bent his head to kiss her and Cindy met the touch of his mouth on hers with a fiery response. Blake's lips seemed to scorch her, to brand her as his body covered hers.

Gone were all feelings of resentment about his tricking her into coming here, and of his restraining her from leaving.

At this second he was everything she wanted in the world.

When he entered her, there was a moment of discomfort. She was no virgin—but it had been so long . . . But as Blake began to move, a slow, rocking motion that brought her to ecstatic life, the past eased away to the present, and disappeared from her mind.

Even in his aroused state Blake did not spare his consideration for her. The signals she sent out were heeded with unfailing sensitivity for her needs; he gave her as much pleasure as she gave him. And when together they reached fulfillment, Cindy experienced a flooding sensation of indescribable pleasure—a depth of sensual enjoyment she had never known before that had her shuddering and crying out his name.

As the labored beating of their hearts blended as Blake lay heavily against her. "You're wonderful," he breathed, his lips soft against her ear.

Still caught in the hazy mists of passion Cindy experienced a growing pressure to confide in him—to admit the undeniable attraction she felt for him.

"What is it, sweetheart?" Blake asked as he started to roll to his side, pulling her with him. His voice was full of tenderness and concern. "Is something . . ."

But as he spoke, a sudden knocking on the cabin's front door caused Prince to begin barking.

Blake's body tensed in surprise, his fingers digging unknowingly into the soft flesh of Cindy's shoulders, a quick frown settling on the ridge of his brow.

The knocking sounded once again, and, correspondingly, Prince's barking became even more furious.

It took just such a jolt to pull Cindy back to reality, and, as a result, an icy chill caused her to stiffen. Good God, what had she done? She looked at Blake with a dawning horror.

Blake met her gaze. "Cindy?" he questioned, but was prevented from saying more by the sound of a woman's voice.

"Blake, come on! I haven't got all night!"

Cindy's gaze darkened even more.

"You'd better go," she whispered huskily.

Blake's frown increased.

"*Blake!*" The feminine voice came again. "I know you're in there, Blake."

A harsh imprecation passed through Blake's tightly held lips as he quickly levered himself up from the bed. While he pulled on his faded jeans, his brown gaze swept over Cindy. Where before it had been filled with warm promise and desire, it now held several emotions, irritation being the most prevalent, with puzzlement and regret the remaining companions.

The banging sounded again, and with another muttered curse Blake turned to stride through the doorway, his athletically muscled form silhouetted against the muted glow of the lamp reaching into the hall from the living room.

Cindy lay where he had left her, her violet eyes dazed, her mind replaying every action she had made over the past fifteen minutes. She couldn't believe what had happened! She couldn't believe she had been so wanton! She moaned and turned her face to the wall, drawing her knees upward and clasping her crossed arms over her bare breasts.

Then the sound of the woman's voice came nearer. Blake had let her inside!

Galvanizing fear shot through Cindy's body. She couldn't let herself be found like this! On Blake's bed with nothing on! She had more pride than that! She slipped back into her discarded dress almost as fast as Blake had his jeans, and with trembling fingers tried to bring some order to her tangled hair.

But the woman came no nearer; she remained in the living room and Cindy expelled a shaky breath. She couldn't decipher the words being exchanged, but a soft tinkling laugh floated through the air.

The laughter only underscored Cindy's growing dismay. She felt like crying. How could she have allowed such a thing to happen? She was an idiot! A fool! Blake Michaels didn't care for her. And she certainly didn't care for him. So how could things have gotten so far out of control? Especially her control. Cindy bit down hard on her bottom lip.

She didn't like to think of herself as a woman starved for sex, but that was how she had acted. Had she somehow given Blake that impression, had she unconsciously vibrated with some kind of code? No—that was impossible. She had never let things go anywhere near so far with any other man since the breakup of her marriage. And the introduction to sex David had given her had not made her miss it; there wasn't really all that much to it anyway. A rush of heat warmed her skin from her toes to her scalp. At least she hadn't thought there to be that much, she amended.

Still, it was hard for her to believe what had occurred, had indeed occurred. She moved toward a nearby bureau on which rested a small mirror, and with a somewhat reluctant hand reached out to bring it close until she could study her dim reflection in its silver-backed surface.

Deep dark splashes of purple looked back at her—portals to a mind that rebelled at an unknown weakness, yet was at the same time forced to accept it because of the evidence now presented. Her hair was tumbled, her cheeks flushed, her lips red and crushed looking, her eyes mysterious with a knowledge relearned and, in the process, added to—and in the background the disturbed covers on the bed.

Cindy thumped the mirror back into place. Damn him! Damn Blake Michaels! Why did he ever have to be born?

Another feminine laugh echoed by a masculine chuckle roused Cindy from her thoughts.

She couldn't stay here!

With determination in every step Cindy marched from Blake's bedroom, intent on locking herself in her own. But when it came time to cross the threshold that opened into the living room—an accomplishment which had to be done in order to attain the safety of her room—she stopped. She couldn't just walk past; she would be seen. And, above all things, she didn't want that—not when she looked exactly what she was: a woman who had just participated in a thoroughly satisfying, at least at the moment, act of love—or, rather, raw sex. Cindy's stomach tightened as she faced the truth, although her spirit rejected the words.

She tried to make herself invisible against the wall, waiting, estimating. It would take only a second at the most for her to bolt by. And if she timed it perfectly . . .

With her heart thumping loudly in her ears and her breath held in case it rattled, Cindy leaned forward to peer carefully around the wooden frame.

Blake was standing before the unused fireplace, and posed across from him was a slender woman whose long length of auburn red hair fell almost to her waist in loose waves. The woman had a hand resting pleadingly on Blake's forearm. Neither was speaking at that moment. Instead, Blake was looking down with a tender expression and the woman was gazing up at him. So since they both seemed to be so absorbed . . .

Cindy took a step forward, ready to throw herself across the empty space. However, she hadn't planned for Prince. The large dog was already on the alert, watching Blake and the woman. The slight movement in the doorway instantly caught his attention.

Oh, God, no! Cindy wailed to herself as she saw his vigilant expression. *Please, don't let him bark!*

But Prince had something else in mind. Since he was now fully awake, and so, it seemed, was the rest of the household, and since she had been a part of that household for almost two days, to his brain, it was now time he tried to make friends with this stranger.

In horrified fascination Cindy watched as the thick weight of the dog's tail began a tentative friendly wag. Then, on not being rebuffed, the animal pushed to his feet and began a slow amble toward her.

Go back! Go back! Cindy wanted to shout, but she remained mute. Maybe if she disappeared again, he would not keep coming toward her. She jerked back behind the door frame.

Prince was stalwart. A little exhibition of coyness by his quarry did not deflect him. Continuing his lumbering gate, the dog came to a halt at Cindy's side. Then, with an expectant *woof,* which was only a slight puffing of hairy cheeks, he reared back, and in the best mastiff fashion pounded his huge front paws on Cindy's shoulders. Cindy staggered backward then forward under the weight.

Needless to say, this commotion drew the attention of the two people in the living room. They looked over in time to see Cindy's face being vigorously cleaned by Prince's huge tongue. In desperation—it felt something like being washed with a fire hose—Cindy cried out, trying to make the dog stop.

Prince gave several more loving laps before he was satisfied. Then, with cumbersome grace, he dropped his front paws onto the floor and stood, glancing toward Blake for approval.

Cindy's reluctant eyes followed the direction of the dog's gaze. She met two matched pairs of cinnamon-shaded eyes—one widened in shocked surprise and the other dancing merrily with wicked enjoyment.

All Cindy could do at that moment was smile weakly and try to make the best of what could prove to be only a horribly embarrassing situation.

CHAPTER SIX

In the past the quickness of Cindy's tongue had almost always gotten her through tough situations. Certainly it had helped with men who took her firmness as a gimmick to further spur their advances. But now, when she really needed to say something sharp and witty in order to save as much of her pride as was not already shredded, nothing came. Her mind was a vast wasteland of useless gibberish.

"Did I interrupt something, Blake?" the woman asked, her amazement having changed to dry humor as she inspected Cindy's disheveled form.

"You've always interrupted when I least wanted you to, Ronnie. You've been a pain since the day you were born and I had to give up my crib."

The woman laughed and Cindy stared at her. Yes, she could see the resemblance. Both had the same classically molded features, though the woman's were softer, more delicate. Both were tall, the woman coming to Blake's chin rather than barely to his shoulder as she herself did. They had the same coloring, the same shade of eyes, the same smile. Only the woman was lightly freckled and her hair was more tinged with flame.

"Sorry," she replied lightly, not the least perturbed by his accusation.

"Liar. You enjoyed every minute of it. Even when I

snuck into the nursery and shook your bed, trying to make you fall out. You just gurgled and laughed."

"Men do make such fools of themselves, and they start at such an early age."

Blake started to laugh and patted the hand that was still resting on his arm.

The woman allowed that action then leveled her gaze on Cindy, who throughout this entire exchange had continued to stand in exactly the same spot where she had been discovered.

"Well, aren't you going to introduce us?" the woman prompted her brother.

Blake's smile increased as his eyes came back to rest on Cindy's still form.

"Of course." The words were drawled as he moved away from his sister's touch. He moved to take Cindy's hand and pulled her unresisting body farther into the room.

Cindy seemed unable to control her own feet. She wanted to run—back to her room, into the bathroom, out into the forest—be anywhere but here!

"Cindy, this is Veronica, my sister," he added unnecessarily. "And, Veronica, this is Cindy, my . . . er . . . a . . . secretary."

On that lame note and with her knowing how rumpled she appeared in comparison to Veronica's neatly turned out self, Cindy could have gladly crawled into the nearest hole. Instead she gave a strangled, "Hello," which might have come from a lamp for all the response it got.

Veronica looked her over in amusement, from her tangled black hair and disturbed clothing to her bare feet—in her hurry she had forgotten her shoes—and a soft chuckle emerged from her throat.

"You'd better have care, brother mine. Or else all those

little eyes and ears who just can't wait for your next words, not to mention their parents, might learn what a lecher you are."

"What those little ears don't know won't hurt them," Blake responded and, smiling devilishly, squeezed Cindy's hand.

Cindy jerked her hand away and sent him a frigid glance.

Again the energy was wasted. Blake shocked her even more by continuing. "Actually you've caught us out in a secret, Ronnie, one we weren't ready to tell anyone yet. But since it's you"—he snaked a long arm out to rest on Cindy's shoulders—"we're going to be married."

Cindy could barely believe her ears. She snapped her head around to look at him incredulously. His sister did the same.

"Aren't you going to congratulate us?" Blake hinted broadly.

When Veronica remained silent, stunned, Cindy opened her mouth to perform a heated protest.

"We're not engaged! We're not anything! We—"

Blake shut her up by swooping his head and applying a smothering kiss.

When she was released, Cindy started to sputter but was interrupted by Blake's husky reminder.

"I've already proposed—"

"But I didn't accept!" she shot back.

"A little thing like that has never stopped me before."

His teasing tone was Cindy's undoing. She twisted free of his hold and turned to face him, her hands perched angrily on her hips. It was all she could do not to rake her fingernails down his tanned cheeks. And to think that a few minutes ago she had been in his bed, actually wanting him . . . wanting his possession . . . letting him possess her.

A wave of crimson shame flooded Cindy's skin, making Veronica arch a brow in inquiry. Cindy saw that look out of the corner of her eye but ignored it.

"It will this time," she retorted through clenched teeth.

Blake rubbed the skin of his chin thoughtfully. "No, I don't think so," he disagreed.

"I do!"

Another voice cut into their conversation. "I don't." It was Veronica. "My brother's right. The word *no* never has stood in his way if he truly wants something. He has got to be one of the most stubborn, as well as the most patient, men I have ever had the misfortune to meet—which is a terrible combination, especially for the women in his life."

Cindy remained still, deeming silence her best ally. Two against one weren't very good odds.

On observing the stubborn set to Cindy's chin, Veronica turned to her brother, an unspoken message passing between them. Then she shifted to another subject entirely, "So what do you think? And if you like the idea, will you help?"

"I don't know." Blake's amused eyes settled back onto Cindy. She raised her chin, causing his amusement to deepen.

"Well, we've got to do something! Mom wanders around her house like some sort of living shadow, and she spends hours just sitting in Dad's old studio. She's just wasting away, Blake. If we don't get her to snap out of it soon, well . . ."

All the amusement left Blake's face as he shifted his full attention back to his sister.

"I'm not sure if a party would help."

"Of course it would!" Veronica insisted. "It will keep her mind off the fact that this is her first wedding anniversary without Dad."

"But a party?"

"It would be the absolutely best thing to do. Get the entire family together. Surround her with love. I know we can never be a substitute for Dad, but we can't let her keep moping. It's been six months. Please, Blake!"

A frown darkened Blake's brow as he conceded. "Maybe you're right. I had a hard time believing how far she's come down since the last time I saw her."

"And it's not going to get better unless we do something."

"Again, you're probably right."

Veronica flashed a brilliant smile. "I'm glad I have a witness. My brother has finally conceded that I actually have a brain or two in my head."

"Don't get too excited. I said *maybe.*"

"Ah, but that's a giant concession."

Blake gave her a superior look which caused Veronica to grin happily. Then a thoughtful pucker replaced the smile. "We'll have to work fast—their anniversary is next Monday."

"Don't say we."

"But, Blake, I can't do it all alone!"

"Since when?" he returned with seeming callousness, but the twinkle in his eyes belied any harshness.

"Oh, Blake!"

"Don't 'oh, Blake' me. I know what a dynamo you are—*and* that you love to plan parties. I'd only be in the way, not to mention that I have more than enough work to do here. Cindy and I both do."

At that Cindy, who had thought herself forgotten, stiffened.

"I thought that maybe Cindy could . . ." Veronica began.

"No. Cindy stays here. She really is my secretary, you know."

Veronica sighed. "Oh, all right. I suppose I can do it all myself."

"Why don't you call Barbara? She'd probably be glad to lend a hand."

"Take over, you mean! No, I'll do it myself."

"See what I mean?" Blake murmured in a wicked aside to Cindy.

Veronica sent him a speaking glare. "I wonder how you can trade in a relative—if there's a service around that handles that."

"You know you'd never do it. I'm too lovable."

"And so very humble."

"That too.

Veronica began to laugh. "I give up. I've got to run. Ted is due in at the airport at midnight, and I'm picking him up."

"So you thought you'd just drop by—"

"If you'd have a telephone installed out here in no-man's land, I wouldn't have had to."

"Just full of complaints, aren't you?"

"The only complaint I'll have is if you don't show up Monday."

"Don't worry, I'll be there." He glanced at Cindy and corrected himself. "*We'll* be there."

Cindy could remain silent no longer. "Oh, no, *we* won't!"

"Oh, yes, we will."

She glared furiously at Blake. This was the opportunity she had been waiting for. "Veronica, will you take me with you? Now! Please!"

Only Veronica laughed, thinking that she was joking. "If there's one thing I've learned over the years, it's to never interfere in other people's business—especially my brother's. I'm sorry, Cindy. The two of you will just have to work it out."

"But . . ."

Blake took hold of his sister's arm and began to hustle her out of the cabin. "Did you say midnight? It's almost that now. And you have a long way to go."

"Oh, my goodness, is it? But it will take a little time for him to collect his luggage."

"Not that long. You don't want to make him wait."

"No, that's for sure." She looked back over her shoulder. "Bye, Cindy, see you."

Cindy hurried behind them. "Veronica, please. You've got to help me. You're brother is insane! He's keeping me here against my will!"

Blake accompanied his sister down the pathway, Cindy in hot pursuit.

Veronica giggled. "You're not telling me anything I hadn't learned long ago. Blake has always been, shall we say, a little single-minded, when he wants something."

"But I don't want him!"

Veronica was in her car and Blake was shutting the door behind her with finality.

"He's not so bad, not really," the woman advised her. "Give him a chance. You may like him. I've even come around to liking him myself . . . most of the time."

"Good-bye, Ronnie. Don't let us keep you."

At that heavy-handed direction, Veronica started her car. Cindy bolted forward, but Blake jerked her back against him, keeping his arms tightly clasped in a crossed position over her breasts. She tried to twist away, but his strength stopped her.

Veronica's cinnamon eyes, which so matched her brother's, looked at them appraisingly, then she confided,

"Blake, this time you may have more work cut out for you than you can handle."

Blake chuckled softly. "No, I don't think so."

Veronica gave him a doubtful look then suggested, "Why don't you come into Houston early Monday? We haven't seen nearly enough of you this trip."

"We may just do that," Blake answered.

"Okay. See you then."

Blake kept his hold on Cindy, keeping her back pressed tightly against his long length. With lessening hope Cindy watched as her chance at freedom disappeared into the darkness of night.

For the next several seconds Blake remained motionless as he too watched his sister drive away, then as if the closeness of Cindy's body brought back recent memories, he bent his head and began to nuzzle the side of her neck.

Cindy tried to pull away. She didn't want him to touch her; she certainly didn't want him to kiss her. And she didn't want the melting feeling she was beginning to experience to go on.

Blake paid little mind to her straining protests. His lips ran smoothly over her skin, finding a path beneath her hair, onto her shoulder, up to her ear. With gentle intimacy his teeth nibbled on her earlobe, his breath coming warm and soft.

Again Cindy tried to tear herself away, but this time it was not just to extract herself from Blake's possession. She was running terrified from herself! Her body was alive to every molecule of his. She felt his warmth, the hardness of the muscles of his chest, of his thighs . . .

When his grip loosened a degree, Cindy thought that at last she had won a concession, but in this she was proved to be mistaken. Instead of freeing her as she had hoped, he was once again pulling her slight weight from the ground and cradling her in his arms.

"Put me down!" she demanded, half angry, half panicked. He merely smiled.

He was successful in carrying her only until they were near the porch. That was when Cindy's resolve that a replay of their earlier intimacy was not going to happen finally won out. She had twisted and jerked until she made it impossible for him to contain her. And when she alighted on her feet, she tore away, uncaring of where she was going.

She was running pell-mell into the forest when Blake caught up with her a dozen steps later.

"Cindy, wait!" she heard his husky voice call just before the grip of his fingers caught in some of the billowing material of her skirt.

Immediately she was pulled to a stop and folded into his arms.

"I won't hurt you, Cindy . . . I won't ever hurt you . . ."

Cindy couldn't move. Tears were sparkling in her eyes and her breath was labored, coming in gulps. Wouldn't she ever be free?

Then he was lifting her chin gently with his forefinger and thumb, and slowly bending his head until he could kiss her lips.

For a time Cindy just stood there, her emotions a whirlpool of jumbled sensations. Then gradually the warmth and demand of his firm mouth drove all thoughts from her mind!

When his lips left hers to glide along the curve of her cheek, the tip of his tongue claimed the escaped moisture of her tears.

Cindy shuddered uncontrollably at the sensual gesture,

her arms coming out to wrap around his waist, her fingers massaging the strong muscles of his naked back, feeling them move as they strained her to him. His skin was like rich golden satin! Yet it was alive! So alive!

She gave a soft moan as he moved to release the first few buttons of her dress so that one of his hands could more intimately cup her breast, the palm warm and glorying in its capture of the small bounty. When he heard the small pleasured sound she gave, Blake's lips returned to fasten urgently back onto hers, his body drinking thirstily of all she was willing to give . . .

For mindless seconds Cindy was lost in a wonderland of sensation, never giving thought to wanting to be found —not unless it was by Blake, who had the ability to take her away from herself, away from her fears. He seemed able, at will, to play on her emotions until they reached a crescendo of bursting need!

Then suddenly she knew that she had to stop; she couldn't let this go on! All it would take would be one small step and she would be past the ability to control herself. She was almost beyond that point now!

She liked the taste of him, the feel of him, the knowledge that he liked it when she ran her hands through his hair, over his shoulders, along the hard flexed muscles of his arms. But it had to stop! It had to! She couldn't afford to let him get close to her again! She didn't even like him!

As Cindy made the gargantuan effort to pull away, both of their breathing was ragged. To save herself, she made a desperate lunge for the only safety she could find: the display of anger.

"Don't do that ever again!" she hissed, her words shaky from the depth of her disturbance.

A cooling breeze had sprung up to rustle the tops of the tall pine trees, causing them to sway gracefully as if in an aerial ballet; tree frogs increased their cry for rain . . . Until that moment Cindy had been unaware of any of it, but now it seemed so much a part of the moment, a reflection of the turbulence in her own soul.

Blake took a deep resigned breath, letting it out slowly. His features, in the dim light, looked faintly grim.

"Why not? You like it."

Cindy shook her head, but it was not wholly a denial. She knew what he was saying was true—but she couldn't afford to admit it! Not to him! His ability to touch her so deeply frightened her!

Neither of them paid any attention to the large drops of rain that were starting to break loose from the clouds above and fall sporadically about them.

"Admit it, Cindy. You like it as much as I do."

"No!"

"More then?"

"*No!*" Cindy searched for something else with which to berate him. "How could you have told your sister that we're going to be married? How could you?"

"It was easy. It's the truth."

"No, it's not!"

"Would you rather have let her go away thinking that we're just sleeping together? Because, I can assure you, that was exactly what she thought. Ronnie isn't exactly slow off the mark. She knew what she had interrupted."

In her anger Cindy started to stammer. Finally she mastered her stuttering to protest, "You're not being fair!" She felt so damn impotent.

"Haven't you heard the old cliché that all's fair in love and war?" The easy humor was now coming back into his voice.

"And this is?" she asked pointedly.

"Why love, of course," he returned smugly.

Cindy wanted to bash him. Honestly, he was the most obnoxious man! If she were to compare him to her ex-husband, in some ways he made even David look good. And that was saying a lot!

"Go to hell, Blake Michaels!" She had had enough of him.

"Will you come with me?" he teased, not taking her the least bit seriously.

"Only if I can use the pitchfork—on you!"

"I'm not sure if the devil truly has one."

"Then I'll bring my own," Cindy grated.

Blake gave an appreciative laugh and reached out as if to draw her into his arms.

Cindy jumped back a step. "I meant what I said—don't touch me again."

"Is it because when I touch you, you don't want me to stop?" he asked, then proceeded to prod softly. "Have you ever asked yourself why?"

That question hit a little too close to the truth for Cindy's comfort, and it unsettled her. And she didn't like to feel unsettled. It was so deficient a way to be when she needed every spare speck of confidence she could muster in order to protect herself.

"I never question myself," she returned haughtily.

"You don't like what you find, eh?"

"No."

"I didn't think so."

Cindy cursed inwardly because she had laid herself wide open for that one. "No!" she retorted, then made as if to move away. "I make it a practice not to ever answer to anyone."

Blake let her take several steps before he decided to follow.

"You must have a pretty lonely existence."

Cindy didn't answer but kept on walking back to the cabin and in through the front door which had been left wide open. Prince was lying on the rug before the fireplace, and he looked up sleepily. She gave him only a passing glance, reflecting irritably on the fact that at least someone could rest around here, and knew that as far as she was concerned, precious little sleep would follow her eventual reincarceration in her room.

Blake followed her into the hall. He stopped as she started to turn toward her room and away from his. "Are you a lonely person, Cindy?"

Cindy's lips firmed. She would be damned if she would answer. No matter what she said, he would twist it to suit his purposes.

With regal determination she sailed into her room and shut the door. But queenly behavior could do nothing to stop the echo of his words. Lonely. Was she lonely? Had she been lonely for a very long time? She threw herself onto the bed. She had never thought of herself as particularly needing people. For most of her life she had been on her own.

Her father had died when she was small and her mother had been forced to work long hours in order to make enough money for them to get by. Out of necessity she had spent many hours in solitary play, as only children become accustomed to doing when there are no other children close by. In school she had made a number of friends, but only a few of them were really close.

With David she had thought to have at last found her soulmate—which was a laugh. Not that David was bad—he was just weak. Weak and selfish. He had made a mockery of their wedding vows: to love, to cherish. David didn't know the meaning of the words. He had presented one face to the outside world and another one entirely to her

. . . after they married. She had been able to take his abuse for only one year.

But did that make her lonely?

If she had to choose over again, whether to stay with her husband or divorce him as she had, she would choose divorce any time. Being a punching bag for an insecure man's temper tantrums after he had drunk enough to lower his inhibitions she would never condone.

Yet, there were times when that old longing came, when her soul cried out for, ached for, something she could not name. Was that loneliness?

The rain that had been only thinking about falling, sending out test drops to scout the area, suddenly made up its mind, and Cindy, lying on her bed, listened to it pepper the roof, the leaves of the trees outside, and the packed sand over which the bracken of the woods resided.

Just as she had thought, she slept little that night. Repeated visions of the previous evening's activities kept besieging her mind, and she tossed restlessly in a vain attempt at attaining rest.

Shame was her primary emotion; she wasn't a woman who fell into a man's bed at the drop of a hat. She never had been. David was her first sexual partner and that had been after they were safely married. And after their split, she had done her best to run, fast, in the opposite direction of any man who's objective it was to get her anywhere near a bed.

So how had Blake managed to countermand her determination? And do it in such a way that she was an active participant?

A bright flush stained Cindy's cheeks, and she was glad that she was alone. She had enjoyed being touched by him, being taken. She had even relished it. Even thinking about it now had the power to arouse. He seemed to have some kind of hold over her that numbed whatever inhibitions she might try to create to form a barrier between them.

And he was still talking about marriage! Did he actually mean it? He had told his sister—but possibly she was just as mentally incompetent as he. Derangement did run in families.

Cindy shifted in her bed and rearranged the pillow under her head. As if she would marry him! The idea was ridiculous. She was independent; she needed no one. Her life was going on perfectly fine as it was. She had already had one dose of marriage and sometimes it seemed as if she'd never completely healed. Her only regret was that she would never know the experience of motherhood.

Suddenly Cindy sat up in the bed. Oh, God! A child. Blake had used no precautions, and neither had she. Quickly her mind did some fast calculations, and she breathed a tentative sigh of relief. The odds of there being no pregnancy were in her favor.

But that wasn't to say that the fact would hold true forever. It was a sure bet that it would not. She had to insure that a repeat of yesterday's performance never happened again. The pitiful example of her ability to resist had been more than adequately proven last night. So she went back to her original plan. She had to get away! And get away fast. Only then would she feel safe—from both herself and him—and be able to go about the business of trying to reconstruct her life.

The downpour of the night before had left little evidence of its existence on the outside world, save for a damp freshness that pervaded the air of the forest.

Cindy greeted the new day with determination. She had decided just before getting up that she would tear the cabin apart if she had to in order to find her keys. They had to be here somewhere. He couldn't have eaten them! And she had been handed a perfect opportunity to search. On leaving her room, she realized that Blake was nowhere to be found. He was gone as was Prince, and she deduced that they must be out for an early morning walk.

A lot of good that had done her though; so far the hunt had yielded little. She had looked everywhere! And still no keys. She began to wish that she had taken better advantage of Blake's absence. She could have been a far distance down the road by now. The only thing that stopped her was that she knew she would make better and more efficient time in her Datsun. Then she would be completely rid of him, and not wondering what avenue to use to regain possession of her car. Another reason was that if she left it here, he could take her doing so as a coquettish maneuver to guarantee their meeting again. And Lord knew, she didn't want that!

Cindy straightened from her inspection of the flour canister. She had checked everything twice and had canvassed every conceivable hiding place. There was only one area left to look. She had saved it for last, although logically she should have started there—Blake's room.

She had shied away from going back because of the memories it held. She didn't want to remember anymore. She wanted to blank out what had happened yesterday from her mind. She didn't want to see the bed where . . .

A minor tremor ran up Cindy's spine, which she instantly quelled. She could face anything if she had to. She was strong.

With commendable calm yet with her emotions churning in her stomach, Cindy moved quietly toward the hall and his room. One hand came out to push the partially opened door farther open. Nervously she entered. Her eyes went automatically to the bed, as if it were a magnet. Quickly she averted them.

Drawing a trembling breath, she forced herself to ignore the pounding of her heart and get on with the business at hand. If she was acting like a burglar, it was only because he was making her do it. And it wasn't as if she was looking for something that was not her property. She had a right to search all she wanted, where she wanted.

She marched over to the bureau and pulled open a drawer. With hurried efficiency she went through the rolled-up socks and neatly folded underwear. Then, finding nothing, she closed the one drawer and pulled out another. She was on her knees, searching the third, when suddenly she became aware that she was no longer alone. There was a presence in the doorway and she knew with dreadful premonition that it was Blake. Reluctantly she glanced up. He was leaning against the door frame, as if he had been there for some time. His arms were crossed over his chest, and he was watching her intently.

"Did you lose something?" His words were dry, ironic.

Cindy decided to brazen it out. After all, what did she have to lose?

"You know damn well what I've lost. Where are they, Blake? The game is wearing a little thin."

Blake straightened and dropped his arms, a hand coming to rest on one lean hip. "What game? I'm not playing any game."

Cindy's lips tightened and in disgust she turned back to what she was doing. She continued to rifle through the drawer until she heard a jingling sound coming from where Blake still stood.

"Is this what you want?" he asked innocently, yet with an edge to his voice.

For a moment Cindy seemed incapable of movement,

then she quickly scrambled to her feet. Automatically she took a step forward, a hand outthrust. Then she stopped short as the jingling ceased and Blake smoothly slipped the keys into the right front pocket of his jeans.

"I'm afraid that if you want them, you're going to have to come get them."

Cindy stared at him blankly for several seconds. She started to move forward once again, then, as before, she stopped. She couldn't do that! As much as she wanted her keys, she couldn't go searching for them in his snugly fitting jeans! The action would be too intimate. Too . . . disturbing. It didn't take much for her to remember the feel of his leanly muscled body, or the way the satiny-smooth texture of his bronze skin had moved against her own.

Cindy swallowed tightly. She felt like an animal at bay.

When she remained motionless, Blake began to stroll leisurely into the room.

Cindy didn't budge. She seemed to be mysteriously fastened to the spot. Her feet could have been lodged in twin weights of lead for all that she could make them function.

Blake stopped walking only when he was standing directly across from her. One long-fingered hand came out to tip her chin gently, making her look up at him.

"I'm not the one playing games, Cindy," he said softly, meeting her dark violet gaze. "It's you." His thumb made slow, sensual circles on her jaw. "If you'd just admit what we both know is true, we'd be a lot better off. I want you, Cindy. And you want me. I know it. I've known it from the beginning. If you'd just stop being so stubborn. We need each other."

Resisting a swamping rush of her feelings was hard, but Cindy somehow managed to retain enough of her sensibilities to mutter a defiant "No!"

Blake gave a deep regretful sigh. "There seems to be only one way we can agree . . ." He slowly bent his head to place his mouth against hers.

The kiss was soft, a gentle moving of lips on lips. Tantalizing, promising more . . . Cindy's blood began to course madly through her veins. She was in danger of losing her detachment again. She liked the taste of him, the feel of him; he called out to something basic concealed deep within her. If she didn't break away soon, she would succumb again. And where would that get her? Would it solve any of her problems—or would it only add more? She knew the answer without hesitation.

She jerked her mouth away from his and took several steps back until she accidentally bumped into the opened bureau drawer. The wood scraped her leg, but she was in no state of mind to notice, just as she had stopped noticing her knees when a greater worry appeared. She had to concentrate fully in order to come out of this situation unscathed.

"Denying it is only hurting us both." Blake made no attempt to come after her, but his eyes watched her every move.

"The only thing that will hurt me is you!" she cried, the sentence bursting out without thought.

"And why is that?" he demanded immediately.

For a moment Cindy was at a loss for words, then she retaliated with a stilted, "If you think, that because I went to bed with you once, I'm going to do it again . . ."

"I think you will."

Cindy's eyes flashed. "Well, you're wrong."

"I could very easily prove that I'm not."

Cindy watched him warily. She waited for him to make a move to come toward her, but still he did not.

"I'm not that kind of woman!" was all she could come up with to defend herself.

"I know that."

His answer threw her. "You know that?" she repeated.

"Of course."

"But—but what about yesterday?"

"I see nothing wrong with an engaged couple making love."

Cindy gave an exasperated sigh. He was still on that! "We're not engaged," she persisted stubbornly. "And we didn't make love. We had sex!"

"Love, Cindy," he corrected her. "We made love."

"How can you say that?" she demanded. "Love . . . love is caring!"

"I care for you."

"But you don't know me! You don't know anything about me!"

"I know enough."

Cindy began to shake her head. Possibly there was only one way to end this.

"Whether you do or don't makes no difference—because I don't care for you."

He actually seemed to be hurt by her denial.

"That's only your intellect talking. I've been in contact with your soul. Maybe one day you will be too."

How did a person counteract that? Cindy began to bluster. "I don't—"

Blake cut her off, as if suddenly becoming tired of the fight. "I'm a patient man, Cindy. But my patience is not unending. It can wear out."

Cindy continued to look at him, at the unaccustomed weariness in his eyes. Her gaze traveled over him. He looked exactly how she felt. Had he had as little success in finding sleep last night as she?

When she remained silent, Blake reached out to grasp her shoulders and turn her toward the door. One hand moved to her back, the fingers warm against material of her blouse. He guided her through the doorway and steered her toward the kitchen.

At last he asked, "What would you like to eat for breakfast? Do pancakes sound good?"

As if in a dream, Cindy found herself nodding. She didn't know what to make of what had just happened. Something had changed, but she wasn't sure what . . . and didn't know if she wanted to examine the situation closely enough to find out.

CHAPTER SEVEN

A disinterested observer witnessing the happenings in the cabin over the next few days could be excused for pausing and scratching his head in bewilderment. And, looking back, Cindy couldn't say that she would blame him. She didn't totally understand everything that had occurred herself.

As good as his word, Blake had prepared their breakfast. They had eaten in a strained silence, then he had cleaned up while Cindy went restlessly to her room. She remained there until approximately midday, her mind a jumble of mismatched thoughts as she tried to reason out what she should do next. A clear idea never came.

Then, out of sheer boredom, she had wandered from her room and found Blake sitting on the sofa in the living room, a portable electric typewriter placed on the coffee table in front of him, a thick stack of papers to his side. He was one-fingering his way with painful slowness.

Only a professional typist knows how irritating such an activity can be. And Cindy was no exception. After watching his struggles for several long minutes, she could stand it no longer.

"If you keep on at that rate, you might get that typed by next summer," she had remarked dryly, enjoying being able to make an indisputable thrust at him.

Blake looked over at her, a quizzical expression in his brown eyes. "I told you I couldn't type."

"I believe it," she murmured.

He turned back to his hunting and pecking.

Finally Cindy moved to stand beside him. His product was a sad sight to see.

"Is that going to be mailed out?" she asked, appalled.

"My editor needs it as soon as I can get it to him." He didn't pause in his hot pursuit of an *o*.

"I hope he has good eyes."

Blake found the letter and pressed it, but as well as touching the *o* tapped the *p* and the end result was a clash of keys that had to be unsnarled, and the copy had a beautiful imprint of a little of each—with shading. Blake gave a grunt of dissatisfaction and changed to what looked to be his favorite key. He x'ed out the entire word. The correction fit perfectly with the rest of the page's decor.

Possibly he had planned all of what then came to pass, possibly he had not, but Cindy soon found herself seated at the table, her fingers flying over the typewriter keys, and his mess a neatly crushed paper ball at her side.

Within the next half hour she had been moved to a more comfortable desk and chair, and she had spent the following three days positioned firmly in place.

Exactly when her urgent desire to get away had been supplanted as her first priority, she didn't know, but she soon found herself immersed in the story of twin boys who were involved in an intrigue surrounding the construction of a nuclear power plant in southern California as told by strong dark pencil strokes.

What made the situation even more confusing, yet at the same time palatable, was that Blake seemed to have declared a unilateral truce. No longer did he pester her with his thoughts on marriage or her resistance to the idea.

Instead, he became the perfect employer. He was considerate, easy to please, and seemed grateful for each section of manuscript she presented for his approval.

Cindy sat at the typewriter, the sixth chapter having just been completed, and gave a tired sigh. Her glance shifted to Blake, who was stretched out on the couch. Papers were strewn about, and a yellow legal-size pad was propped on one raised knee as he lay down, his head resting on several throw pillows. A frown was marking his brow, and he was tapping the pencil eraser thoughtfully.

Cindy let her gaze remain on him. She knew it was safe. When he was concentrating on his writing he was oblivious to anything else.

Her eyes took in the long length of his muscular form, unconsciously appreciating the way his dark slacks and cotton pullover fit. His chestnut hair was mussed somewhat, giving evidence of a natural tendency to curl; his bottom lip was tucked in slightly on one side.

Cindy forced herself to turn away. This had to stop. It was beginning to happen with much more frequency as the hours went by. It was as if by his very withdrawal he was laying a trap for her, and she was playing directly into his hands. How stupid could she possibly be? And yet her eyes flickered back and a warm feeling rose from the fire banked deeply in her unconscious, a warmth she seemed helpless to cool.

As she watched, Blake stopped tapping his pencil and began to jot his thoughts down quickly on the pad. When he was done, he sat forward and rubbed a hand along the back of his neck. That movement caused his head to turn, and he caught her fixed gaze upon him.

For the space of several breathless seconds Cindy could not look away. She caught hold of herself only when a small smile began to tilt the carved line of his lips. She jerked her eyes away and pretended to concentrate on the typewriter, rolling another sheet of paper into the carriage and peering hard at the transcript as if involved in deciphering the words starting the next chapter. But all the while she was wholly aware that Blake was getting to his feet and walking toward her. By the time he stopped to look over her shoulder, her heart was thumping a loud signal of alarm.

"You've come quite a way," he commented softly, a dual meaning in the huskiness of his voice.

Cindy refused to look up, afraid that her violet eyes would give away the confusion that was seething within her. She hated this feeling, this crack of vulnerability in her normally sealed shell of reserve. She would not let it continue to widen.

Purposely she took the track of obviousness. "Yes, I have, haven't I?" Her fingers continued to fly, the clatter of the keys offputting to any continued attempt at conversation.

Blake remained standing at her side, and Cindy's nerves tightened even more. It was only by some kind of miracle that her fingers continued to perform their efficient task.

"Don't you think you've done enough for today?" Blake questioned eventually.

"You're the boss. Have I?" She could feel the touch of his eyes on the back of her head.

"At least you've finally admitted that much . . ."

Cindy's fingers stumbled on the keys, causing the same sort of snarl Blake had suffered the last time he had typed. She was in the process of undoing them when Blake's long hand came out and tore the paper from the machine.

"I say you've done enough. You haven't really stopped except to go to bed at night."

"Since you're determined that you're not going to let me

go and that I'm going to have to work for you, I've decided to get it over with as quickly as possible."

That wasn't really the truth. This was the first time such a thought had entered her mind, but Cindy wasn't about to tell him that!

"Mmmm." Blake's answer was noncommittal, but his action was not. He pulled her up from the chair by firmly grasping her shoulders and said, "What you need is a walk, to get out into the sunshine and fresh air."

"What's the matter?" she countered quickly. "Am I developing prison pallor?"

Blake pretended to study her. "You are a little pale around the gills."

Cindy couldn't help the smile she gave. "And you're not exactly Prince Charming either."

Now her nose should have really grown on that one! He was handsome enough to pass for a fairy-tale prince. If only he would act like one!

"Speaking of Prince, would you mind if he came along?"

Cindy hesitated. She didn't exactly remember having agreed herself. But she didn't feel like fighting him. She was tired. Her back ached; her head felt a little muzzy, as if a headache was close to coming on.

"No, I don't mind," she returned.

Blake gave a sharp whistle and Prince, who had been lying in a warm spot where the sun shone through a front cabin window, was instantly ready to go.

If such a large dog could scamper and dance with delight, Prince did. He really was nothing more than a puppy, as Blake had said, Cindy decided. An overgrown one, but he couldn't help it. In his mind he was a cream puff and obviously pictured himself a lap dog.

The forest in the late afternoon held qualities of both

warmth and peace. The heat of the summer sun was still evident but made more tolerable by the sun's lower position, and the total absence of any noise made by humankind seemed almost loud to Cindy. Inside the cabin it was easy to forget that they were in so isolated an area, the gentle hum of central air-conditioning being the same everywhere. But outside there could be no denying their seclusion.

Blake and Cindy walked side by side, Prince gamboling happily through the brush. Without perceptibly directing Cindy, Blake steered their steps toward the pond.

Cindy's nose twitched at the warm pungent smell of fallen pine needles and oak leaves, her eyes settling on the pond. Grudgingly she admitted to its beauty.

The two continued in silence, following a trail which turned into the trees. Blake walked easily, his long athletic gait shortened to allow Cindy a comfortable speed.

She soon found herself relaxing, the muzziness in her head having begun to disappear and the tension of her back and neck muscles unwinding. She chanced a short glance at the silent man by her side. His eyes were focused a short distance along the trail ahead and he looked to be deep in thought, his mind, in all likelihood, traveling with the story he was working on.

Cindy swiveled her gaze forward, a puzzled frown beginning to wrinkle her brow. Blake was a study in contradiction, which shouldn't have surprised her. It was what she had come to expect from men. Yet something about him was different. And it was that very difference that bothered her, reluctant though she was to admit it.

He had taken her—she had taken him. He seemed to accept that it would happen again. But he wasn't pressing the issue.

And he was a children's writer! She couldn't quite yet

accept that fact! Lord knew, he didn't look the part! And, most astounding of all, was the fact that he was good—no, he was excellent. She had been surprised at how intricate a plot he contrived and how tightly the mystery she was typing was woven with characters who seemed to come to life on the page. He wrote for children—young adults actually—as if they were people with thoughts and feelings and not simply nonentities who were reading because someone else, a teacher or parent, was making them. In fact, as she could attest, he probably had his fans among those groups as well, and not just because they were concerned with children. His stories, though vocabulary-conscious for fourteen-year-olds, were fast-paced and exciting and were capable of capturing the adult imagination. So why, she wondered, did he write exclusively for children? With all the talent he possessed he could have made it very big in the adult market, writing the kinds of books that made their authors millions. So why had he limited himself? Didn't money and what it could buy interest him? As far as David had been concerned, there was no other god. Absently Cindy gave a small sigh.

As quiet as the sound had been, it was enough to draw Blake's attention from his thoughts.

"Feeling better?" he questioned, his husky voice making an involuntary quiver run up and down her spine.

Cindy drew her arms across her breasts and hugged herself. "A little."

Blake seemed satisfied. He turned back to the trail and was silent again.

Cindy let the space of several steps go by before she commented offhandedly, "I like the book I'm typing. Was it hard to research?"

Blake looked at her in surprise. Then he smiled, a little self-mocking smile that Cindy found disconcerting.

"A little. But I had a friend in the industry who helped a great deal."

"Oh."

They took another few steps.

"You really liked it?" Blake questioned, as if still unable to believe that she had.

"Yes. I wouldn't tell you I did if I didn't."

"Well, thank you, then. I'm kind of happy with the way it turned out myself."

Cindy chanced another glance at him, and before she quite knew what was happening, she was asking the question that was uppermost in her mind. "Why do you waste your time writing for children?"

Blake stopped, causing Cindy to stop with him. He turned fully toward her and was close enough that she had to tilt her head back to see his face.

"I guess I don't consider that it's wasting my time," he murmured at last.

Cindy met the steady cinnamon-shaded gaze.

"But you could write a best seller! A . . . a blockbuster. Isn't that what they're called?"

A smile flickered over Blake's lips and one eyebrow rose a degree. "That's what they're called, all right," he agreed with wry humor.

Cindy's impatience with his answer must have showed because Blake continued almost immediately, "I like to write for children. They're honest, they're straightforward, and, sometimes, much more discriminating than adults."

"How do you mean?" Cindy asked curiously.

"They won't read garbage. Does that sound egotistical? I don't mean it to. What I'm trying to say is that if the story line doesn't hold them from almost the first page, you can forget about getting them to finish the book. It's a challenge. The writer walks a fine line. He has to balance entertainment along with helping the child learn something about the real world. And they can't feel lectured to. That's the immediate death of a book. A kid can spot a lecture a mile away."

Cindy continued to gaze at him curiously. He was serious about all of this. But, then, had she expected him to be otherwise?

"Have you always written for children? I mean"—she shrugged lightly—"always wanted to?"

Blake laughed. "No. I never dreamed I'd end up doing this. I started out doing what Paul Sawyer does." He named the investment counselor she had been working for when she met him. "I took all the appropriate courses in college . . . a masters in business administration. But after two years on the job, I found that I hated it." He paused, as if thinking of his feeling of long ago. "I just kind of fell into writing. A cousin of mine has twin sons. I played around with writing a few things to send to them when I was away trying to *find* myself." His smile increased, making Cindy's heart double its pace. "And I found out that I was a writer."

Cindy was silent, mulling over what he said. She was just about to phrase another question when Prince, who the last time she had seen him had been sniffing at the edge of the pathway before going off to follow the scent his nose had discovered, set up a growling bark which was a combination of surprise and alert.

When the noise continued, Blake excused himself and walked into the underbrush, following the sound of Prince's growls.

He was gone for only a short time, but Cindy became uncomfortable alone. The sun was beginning to set and the thought of facing more forest animals alone and unprotected didn't appeal to her.

When Blake came back, his shirt had been stripped off and he was carrying something rolled up inside.

Cindy frowned when she saw him. What on earth . . .

Blake moved into position beside her. He looked at his bunched-up shirt then over to her.

"Do you have anything against being a foster mother?"

Cindy blinked. "What?"

"You mentioned rabbits the other day. Well, Prince found a few of the progeny."

Prince, hearing his name, began to circle Blake's feet.

"Rabbits?" Cindy inquired cautiously.

Blake unfolded the edge of the shirt. Inside were four tiny, barely alive little animals. He held them out to her.

"Rabbits," he confirmed.

Cindy stared at them. "I don't understand. Where did you find them?"

"Prince found them," he corrected, covering the pitiful specimens back up again. "Their mother's been killed. He found her too."

Cindy was completely out of her element. "So what can we do about it?

"Not a lot, most probably. But I'd like to try. I don't like to see any animal suffer."

He had turned toward the cabin and was walking back to it more swiftly than they had come. Cindy had to almost run to keep up with him.

"But what can we do?"

"Try to keep them alive."

"But how?"

Never in a million years had Cindy ever envisioned

herself spending time in a log cabin, in the middle of an east Texas pine forest, trying to coax a warm milky liquid into a baby rabbit's mouth with a spoon. But she was doing it. Just as Blake was with another small bundle of frail life.

"It's not working, Blake! I can't get him to open his mouth."

"Just keep trying. Anything you get down him will be better than nothing."

Cindy kept trying. And when she felt she had exhausted her efforts with the one, she carefully deposited him back in the makeshift nest Blake had prepared and withdrew another.

For the next half-hour the two of them worked silently, diligently in partnership and Cindy found that where, at first, she had been hesitant to touch the rabbits, she soon became accustomed to the feel of their soft little bodies. She had never seen a newborn rabbit this closely before. Their eyes were still sealed shut and the silklike fur which covered their skin was so very fine. Their little faces and helpless forms quickly brought her heart into play, and she became just as determined as Blake that they would live.

At the end of the half-hour, when they seemed to have done all they could for the present, Blake leaned back and sighed. "I doubt if they'll make it. They're pretty weak—"

"But we did get a little nourishment into them." Cindy didn't want to hear any negative thoughts.

"Yes, but it wasn't the right kind. They need their mother's milk. They're only a few days old at best."

"You said something was better than nothing," she reminded him, her violet eyes filled with entreaty.

Blake sighed and massaged the back of his neck. "True."

"So . . . ?"

Blake's cinnamon gaze remained steadily upon her, then his hand moved to cover the one she had resting on the table. "So, we'll have to wait and see."

Cindy held his gaze, the warmth of his large hand radiating a comforting heat. "I don't want them to die, Blake."

"Neither do I."

And she knew that he truly didn't. After all, he was the one who had saved them in the first place. Cindy's eyes began to swim with unaccustomed moisture, causing Blake's fingers to tighten in an effort to give silent reassurance, but somehow that action only made the moisture increase, just as did his understanding smile.

Their evening meal was light, neither of them feeling very hungry. And when Blake began his usual job of clearing their dishes from the table, Cindy surprised both herself and him by offering to help.

Blake made no cutting remark but instead accepted her help and in silence they again worked in partnership.

There was little sleep for either of them that night, both having decided to stay up and continue their efforts with the rabbits.

By daybreak even Cindy had to admit that their energies were being wasted. Instead of growing stronger, the babies were becoming noticeably weaker.

"Could—could we take them to a vet?" she burst out at last.

Blake looked up tiredly. "It wouldn't do any good."

"We could try!" Cindy's eyes flashed.

"It's too late, Cindy. It was really too late when we found them. They had been alone too long."

"Then why did we try to save them? Why didn't you

just leave them where they were?" In her impotence Cindy felt as if she had to strike out at someone. And Blake was the nearest available target.

Blake watched her steadily, sleeplessness adding to the fine lines at the sides of his mouth. "Would you have really wanted me to do that?"

Cindy dropped her gaze to the table. "No," she choked.

Blake said no more and neither did she.

Finally, a short time later, Blake shifted in his chair and suggested, "Why don't you go get some rest? There's nothing more to be done here."

Cindy glanced at the box on the table. Inside the rabbits' little chests were moving rapidly, erratically, in an effort to cling to life. Her heart contracted. She would never have thought she could become so attached to anything so fast. But, then, a battle against death drew all earthly creatures closer together, animal as well as human.

Willingly Cindy pushed back her chair. She didn't want to be there when they died. It was running from reality, she admitted. But Blake encouraged her to get some rest and she didn't wish to defy him. In a way she was grateful.

"Yes," she murmured half to herself. Then, "You'll let me know when . . ."

Blake nodded, his eyes solemn. "I'll let you know."

Cindy went tiredly to her room. She lay down on the bed, her eyes staring at the ceiling. But she could find no peace of mind. She turned on her side and determinedly shut her eyes. Still rest would not come. Finally she gave up. She couldn't sleep. Every time she closed her eyes, she saw a tiny rabbit face.

With a deep sigh Cindy rolled from the bed and wandered back toward the kitchen. She would just check, see what was happening.

She stopped as she approached the doorway, the scene

inside the room at first not making sense to her. The box was on the floor, Blake's shirt was laid out on his thighs, and his hands were cupped about what was lying there.

Then she realized what he was doing—he was keeping them warm! In their last few breaths on earth, Blake was reaching out to give them as much comfort as he possibly could! If he couldn't save them, he was going to make their passing as easy as possible.

Cindy quietly backed away, not wanting him to know that she had seen what was essentially a private moment of giving.

With tears filling her eyes she walked softly back into her room and closed the door, her emotions a confusing mixture of chaotic thought. All along she had resented Blake, even to the point of thinking him crazy. He had thrust himself into her life, refused to listen when she told him in as many ways as she knew how that she didn't want to have anything to do with him. He had kidnapped her, forcing her to stay where she didn't want to, forcing her to stay with him, insisting that they would one day marry. He had shown her that she was not as invulnerable as she thought, had acted the complete, dominant male, and now he had to do this! All men were Jekyll and Hydes, but the side she had found they presented to the world at large was always their better one. Just like David they reserved their true self for private moments, and it wasn't very complimentary. From what her mother had told her, her father had been just the same. Cindy didn't remember much about him, but what she did remember was how he had been the life of every party, laughing, kidding, talking to his friends, then when they were alone, he would lose all desire to talk and become morose and hostile. What private hell he put his wife through when their daughter wasn't present, her mother had only hinted at. But Cindy could imagine. In trying to find someone opposite to her father, she had fallen into the trap of making the same mistake.

But Blake! Damn, it was all so confusing! Blake was different. His private side was gentle, not that he had ever been in any way rough with her, not at any time. He had just been persistent, with that stubborn determination about getting what he wanted.

And she had done as he wished, to a degree. Oh, she fought a good fight, arguing back, using every means she had discovered in her years alone to combat what, if she were honest with herself, she could only admit was attraction. Look at what had happened the second night she was here! But she had stayed. And she really couldn't say that it was because he refused to give her her keys. As she had come to realize earlier, for the past three days the idea of escape had not been burning as brightly as before.

Now this had to happen! Cindy thumped her pillow and folded it under her chin. Why did life have to be so darned difficult at times? She had been perfectly happy, dealing adequately within her own world. Then he had to come along to turn everything upside down!

And his remark about her being lonely still rankled! She wasn't lonely; she was independent! She needed no one!

A small frown began to furrow Cindy's forehead. Why were those words beginning to sound more than a little trite, if not downright hollow? She gave the pillow another disgruntled punch.

CHAPTER EIGHT

Not much time had passed before Cindy was startled out of her abstraction by the sound of a soft knock on her door. Quickly she jumped from the bed and hurried to pull it open. Blake stood just outside.

"You told me to tell you." That was all he said. That was all he needed to say.

A lump formed in Cindy's throat, but she wasn't sure if it was for the rabbits or because Blake looked so downcast.

"You did all that you could," she whispered, trying to give him some comfort. She had never seen a man so sensitive before and didn't quite know what to do with him.

"Yeah," he replied gruffly and started to turn away.

Cindy followed. He walked to the door where the box had been placed.

"What are you going to do?" she asked.

"What do you think?"

"Bury them?"

He nodded.

The lump in Cindy's throat tightened even more. If David had been the one to find the rabbits, in the first place he would not have taken care of them, but even if he had, he would not have bothered with anything more than tossing them away in the nearest garbage can.

Blake felt different, and she was beginning to understand him enough to instinctively know that. Without asking if he minded, Cindy followed.

He walked until he came to a spot near the pond then veered off until under the shade of a tall pine. As if understanding in his canine way, Prince dogged their steps without his usual exuberance.

Cindy watched as Blake dug a hole with a large serving spoon from the kitchen. There were no outside tools, or so it seemed.

The rabbits were still wrapped in his shirt, and this he placed in the hole.

When he was done covering it, he turned and saw for the first time that Cindy had come with him. For a moment he seemed disconcerted, as if he had not thought she would be interested. Then a small, rueful smile pulled at the corners of his well-drawn mouth.

"Now you really do think I'm crazy, don't you? I've just proved it."

Cindy returned his gaze. "No. I don't think that."

Blake continued to look at her, and although she couldn't read the expression that had settled in his eyes, she didn't flinch.

Finally Prince, becoming impatient, moved to Blake's side and nudged him, effectively breaking the spell that had suddenly seemed to surround them.

Cindy turned away, slightly embarrassed. She didn't understand what was happening to her. She felt breathless, her knees were shaky. A stray thought flitted into her mind but remained for so short a time that she was barely conscious of its presence.

Blake laughed a little roughly and rubbed Prince behind

the ears. "We've been ignoring you, haven't we, boy? I can't even remember if I fed you last night. Come on, let's get you something to eat." He looked over at Cindy. "And us too. Then I'm for bed."

Slowly Cindy turned to look at him. "Me too," she replied.

Again a little silence sprang up between them, but this time neither allowed their thoughts to show. And Cindy realized that if he misinterpreted her reply, it wouldn't really rankle her. The thought excited her at the same time as she denied it.

Rearranging scheduled sleep is not the easiest thing for a body to do, but Cindy was so tired from her night of acting nursemaid that she fell instantly into a deep slumber and did not awaken until late in the afternoon. And when finally she did make her way back to consciousness, it was to a kind of groggy awareness that made her wonder if it wouldn't have been better not to have attempted to sleep in the first place. She lay in her bed for some time just trying to make the functions of her brain come together with some sort of cohesiveness.

When she felt she had done all that she could along those lines, she slowly pushed back the thin coverlet and, after pulling on her robe, stumbled her way into the bathroom, hoping that a quick shower would help. It did. She emerged fifteen minutes later feeling much better and more able to deal with the world.

Still, the inside of the cabin was quiet and Cindy decided that in all likelihood Blake was sleeping. So instead of immediately making her way back to her room to dress, she drew the short robe a little more securely about her unclad form and padded barefoot into the kitchen. All she needed was a cup of coffee and everything would be perfect. She filled the poppy-colored enameled tea kettle with water, no longer caring that all Blake seemed to stock was instant. The way she felt now, even that would taste of ambrosia.

While she waited for the water to boil, Prince came lumbering slowly into the room. Cindy smiled fondly when his tail began a desultory yet friendly wag.

"You're probably wondering just what the heck is going on, aren't you, boy? Poor thing." As Cindy began to rub the massive head, the tail-wagging became more energetic. She continued to rub when the dog's long tongue came out to lick her wrist in grateful appreciation. "You're not so bad, are you?" she asked, then gave a soft chuckle. "I really was frightened of you when I first saw you. Do you remember that?"

This entire one-sided conversation had been carried on with the sleeping Blake in mind. But it must have been enough to disturb him. He came wandering into the kitchen, a pair of faded jeans hugging tightly to his hips and thighs. He was still minus a shirt. Cindy's eyes ran appreciatively over his bare chest and arms. As she had noted before, he was not overly endowed with chest hair, only a fine sprinkling of it centered over the deep muscles, but he had enough to be termed provocative, and she was glad that the beginning screams of the tea kettle gave her an excuse to look away before he noticed her kindling interest.

Blake yawned and rubbed his jaw before collapsing into a chair.

"Is it good morning or good evening?" he asked, fixing her with a humorous, yet somewhat bloodshot, eye.

"A little of both, it seems," she replied without stopping her movement to take a mug from the rack nailed to the wall above the counter.

"Got enough for two?" he inquired.

Cindy made the mistake of glancing over her shoulder. He looked so good sitting there, slouching somewhat, it was true, but it was a sexy sort of slouch. The twinkle in the cinnamon-brown eyes was pronounced and definitely added to his appeal, as did the slightly mussed chestnut hair and low, husky voice.

Her fingers tightened on the mug. "Of course," she replied, trying to sound unaffected but was dismayed to hear how high and thin her voice came out. She quickly cleared her throat, hoping that if he had noticed, he would put it down to congestion. She busied herself with pouring hot water.

When she turned back around, she caught Blake giving her just as an appreciative perusal as she had first given him, and her face took on a dusky hue. She had forgotten that she was hardly dressed for exhibition, so wholly had she been preoccupied with her reaction to him!

She placed the filled cup on the table and murmured, "I'll go get dressed," not daring to meet his eyes.

"But what about your coffee? I didn't mean to scare you off."

It was just an expression, but he had no idea of how accurately it was beginning to describe her feelings.

"I'll get it later." She strove for offhandedness.

"You can get it now. I have a good memory, Cindy. I already know what you look like under that thing. You don't have to hurry off under some claim of maidenly modesty."

The duskiness in Cindy's cheeks increased, and for one of the few times in their acquaintance, she was speechless. She truly didn't know what to reply. It wasn't maidenly modesty. It was . . . It was . . . She didn't know what. And it disturbed her to be reminded of that night. Especially now, when neither of them was wearing much more clothing than they were then.

"I *want* to get dressed. It has nothing to do with—" she began, only to be interrupted by his, "Then why are you blushing?"

To her disgust she felt the heat intensify.

"I'm hot." It was the first reason that came to mind.

Blake looked barely capable of restraining his laughter at that reply, and Cindy didn't wait around for him to lose the battle. She escaped from his presence and hurried to her room.

When she returned to the kitchen a short time later, now adequately dressed in a blue twill skirt, white blouse, and white sandals, Blake was busy with the preparations for their evening meal. Cindy watched silently for several seconds before coming to stand close by.

A little self-consciously she asked, "Is there anything I can do to help?" She felt as if she had made her point about not doing housework when she was hired as a secretary, and circumstances had changed somewhat. How, she wasn't quite sure. But . . .

Blake tilted his head to consider her. "Are my ears deceiving me or did I hear you offer to lend a hand?"

"You heard right."

A slow smile began to play on his lips. "Do you know how to peel a potato?"

Cindy stared at him. "Of course."

He shrugged. "A man never knows anymore. Some women refuse to do such menial labor."

That was a dig at her previous attitude and she let it pass. She supposed she deserved it. But she couldn't help the slight clenching of her teeth as she retorted, "Show me the potato."

The next thirty minutes were a pleasant experience for

Cindy as was the meal they shared: broiled steaks, scalloped potatoes, green salad, and fresh apples that had been refrigerated, making them cold and crisp.

Cindy sat back replete. Blake did likewise and grinned. "For a woman of your size, you like to eat, don't you?"

Cindy smiled sweetly. "Should I say the same about you?"

"It would be the truth."

"Then I agree with what you said about me."

Blake laughed appreciatively and let his eyes run over her, making Cindy's breath quicken. She moved restlessly in her chair.

After they had cleared away the dishes, Cindy wandered over to the typewriter and flicked through the remaining pages of the chapter she had been working on the day before. She didn't really feel like typing but, short of going back to her room, didn't see how she could pass the next few hours otherwise.

Blake saw her wavering resolve and suggested, "What would you say to playing hooky?"

Cindy turned wide violet eyes upon him. "What?"

"Playing hooky. It is Sunday after all."

"But your deadline—"

"To hell with my deadline. I'm a writer, not a machine."

"But you wouldn't be doing it! I would!"

"And you're not a machine either. Come on." He didn't give her time to search for any more excuses. He took possession of her arm and practically scooted her out the door.

Once on the porch, the grip on her arm lessened until it became one of companionship. She didn't try to shake it loose.

They walked in silence until they came to the pond.

This time, instead of following the trail, Blake guided her toward the water's edge.

Cindy gazed out over the glasslike surface and at the wall of trees surrounding it on the horizon. Again the distinctive smells of the forest assailed her nostrils and, as her ears were becoming more accustomed to the silence, she began to pick out sounds. Tiny birds tittered playfully in branches high off the ground; a woodpecker busily gave a series of hollow knocks in its search to find food beneath a tree's bark. Her city ears were starting to become accustomed to the country. And Cindy found that it was a good feeling.

Much to her surprise, she was beginning to like it here. When compared to cement, the soft bracken cushion lying on top of the sandy soil was beginning to hold its own in desirability. And the air! She could actually breathe! Her lungs had been accustomed to drawing in smoggy city air for so many years, they had not known what to do in a clear fresh atmosphere.

She gave a soft sigh and tipped her head a little to give Blake a sideways glance. He seemed to be appreciating the beauty of the forest just as she. She swiveled her vision back to the pond.

"It's so peaceful . . . so . . ." she mused almost reverently, unable to find more words.

Blake waited for her to finish and when she didn't commented in agreement. "It begins to get to you after a while."

Cindy turned to look at him fully. "You really love this place, don't you?"

"I've known it since I was a boy." He motioned back toward the cabin. "My father and I built that cabin."

Cindy followed the direction of his gaze. "You did?" In

her world, people didn't build their own houses—they contracted for them and let other people do it.

"One summer when I was seventeen." Blake shifted his stance and dropped to sit on the ground beneath a tall pine tree. He patted the earth for Cindy to follow suit, which she soon did.

"Was your father . . . did he know much about building cabins?" she asked tenatively.

Blake allowed a little grin. "No. He was a senior geologist for an oil company."

Cindy tried to work it out. "Then how . . . ?"

"We went to the library and looked it up. You can do that, you know. You can find instructions to build just about anything you want—if you know where to look."

"But surely it took more than that!"

"A lot of hard work. We had to clear the land," he paused as if remembering. "Then we used the trees we cut down to make the logs. We wanted to keep as closely as we could to the ways the pioneers used when they settled east Texas—at least on the outside." Blake picked up a dried pine needle and began to twirl it between his thumb and forefinger. "My dad loved this land. After the cabin was finished, he used to come every weekend that he could and paint. And then when he retired, he would spend weeks at a time. My mother never had cause to be jealous of another woman; she had the forest. Not that she ever was jealous. She loved it too."

Cindy remained silent, thinking of the paintings she had seen.

Blake was content to let the silence run on as well. Then finally he broke it by saying, "I've told you about me, about my family. Now it's your turn."

Cindy gave a little start. She hadn't expected that. And

she never talked about her past. Not to anyone. She shrugged lightly. "I hatched from an egg."

Blake gave an amused chuckle and reached out to cup the back of her neck with a warm hand. He began to massage it gently.

"Now, that I don't believe."

A collection of chills ran repeatedly up and down her back. When he smiled at her like that . . . Cindy drew a deep breath. Maybe it would be all right to tell him something. Then maybe he would stop doing that!

Her plan worked to a certain degree, but he didn't remove the hand. It stayed beneath the strands of her dark hair.

"My father died when I was small. My mother went to work, and she died when I was eighteen. That's all."

Blake considered her thoughtfully. "That's not all."

Cindy shifted her eyes away. "No."

"What?" The rubbing started once again.

Cindy had to swallow. Her entire body was coming alive to his touch.

"I—I was married. It didn't work out."

Instantly the movement stopped. His hand seemed to freeze for a moment. Then it started up again, only this time she could feel that it was an unthinking action, as if he were unaware that he was still doing it.

"Very long ago?" he asked, his tone huskier than usual.

Cindy didn't want to tell but seemed compelled. "Five years."

Blake frowned. "You couldn't have been more than a baby!"

"Nineteen. Old enough."

He absorbed that information. "How long did it last?"

"About a year."

"Do you still love him?"

"No!"

The hand on her neck seemed to relax a degree.

Cindy moved her head, making him aware that she wanted him to stop.

"And what about you? Were you ever married?"

Blake gave a half smile and let his hand fall away. "No . . . Engaged once, but it didn't work out either."

"Did you love her?" Cindy thought it only fair to pay him back in kind. He hadn't hesitated to ask her personal questions.

"Yes."

"Did you break it off or did she?"

"She did."

"Why?"

Blake looked at her quizzically. "You believe in getting your pound of flesh, don't you?"

Cindy held his gaze steadily.

He sighed then answered. "She wanted a nine-to-five man who wore only the best suits and went to only the best places. I found that I didn't want that. I gave her a choice. She didn't choose me." He was quiet for a moment, but Cindy could sense that no hurt remained. "I believe she's been married a couple of times now."

"Have you seen her again since you broke up?"

"Occasionally."

"And?"

He flipped the pine needle back to its place on the ground. "Nothing. I think I had a lucky escape."

He tipped up her chin and leaned close, looking deeply into her eyes.

"Has anyone ever told you that you have the most beautiful eyes?"

The softly spoken words made Cindy's heart begin to pound.

"A man could drown in your eyes," he continued, whispering softly.

Cindy, who was about to go down for the third count herself, silently echoed the thought. Only she was feeling the same about his. Warm brown with darker rings around the edges of the irises. Intriguing little lines radiating outward from the pupils . . .

At first the touch of his lips to her cheek startled her. If she had expected a kiss, it would have been on her lips. But this—this was almost as devastating. His lips were soft and warm and sensual as they slowly passed along the petallike skin to the side of her mouth, drawing her, beguiling her, arousing her in spite of herself, making her want this slow, enticing salute to be more. In the end, it was she who turned and caused their mouths to unite . . . she, who after beautiful seconds of wonderment, caused the kiss to deepen, her lips moving against his with unconscious seduction, responding to the spark of fiery need smoldering deeply within her; she who invaded the warm moistness of his mouth, tasting its nectar-like essence, exploring the silky smoothness of its inner skin, teasing the tip of his tongue with small shallow thrusts of her own.

It was combustion feeding on combustion: the knowledge of her ability to heighten his arousal heightened Cindy's own excitement. The more she received the more she wanted . . .

Blake's fingers moved urgently to the back of her head, threading in the fine dark hair, pulling her closer. His other hand lifted to rest on her upper arm, caressing the flesh with rising intensity.

Cindy couldn't help it; her body melted against him, and slowly, as if it were the most natural thing in the world, they moved with the gravity of the earth and rested upon it. Dried leaves and twigs cushioned their heads, but they were oblivious to them. They could have been of the finest satin. She inhaled the musky scent of the leaves and damp earth as her arms went up to encircle his neck.

The warm movements of their mouths continued as he untangled his hand from her hair and transferred it to trail butterfly touches along the exposed skin where her blouse had come out of her skirt, each smooth stroke increasing the kindled fires that were bursting into raging flames.

Just as he had done, Cindy embarked on a quest for closer contact; she brought one hand away from his neck to run down along his spine, enjoying the hardness and powerful muscularity of his back. She thrilled to the working muscles and straining sinews. She placed her palm on his ribs and felt his deep harsh breath before letting her fingers travel on to the flatness of his stomach . . .

Cindy knew that she should call a halt; knew also that she would, eventually, but she wanted just a few minutes more. For the moment her body had once again mastered her mind, and whether she wanted it to or not, the memory of their previous lovemaking asserted itself and a surge of need to once again consume at least a part of the bitter honey seared through her. As before, she knew it was only a physical reaction, but for the moment, it was an action she welcomed.

She gave a gasp of surprised pleasure when the gentle stroking of his fingers slid up over her midriff and spread to cover one breast. The lacy material of her bra might not have been there for all the protection it gave from his burning touch.

Cindy gave a low moan as he played with the ever hardening peaks. Unconsciously her fingers began to knead the flesh at his waist.

For a moment a thread of sanity returned and she

started to push him away. But a sudden tremor coursing the length of his long body communicated itself vividly and she trembled in quick response.

Blake felt her quiver and pulled his mouth away. But it was only a momentary reprieve. He bent his head to her throat, his lips like molten lava on her overly sensitized skin, his hand going down to brush her skirt aside to caress her thighs, a knee raising to cover one of her own.

His words were like broken velvet when he murmured, "God! Cindy, I . . ."

It was like trying to swim against a powerful current . . . but resurrected rationality somehow gained control. Maybe it was the compulsion behind his words that allowed her the one second needed to restrain her tempestuous senses . . . Maybe it was returning fear . . . She didn't know. But she responded to his huskily spoken words with a desperate cry of "No!" The denial was to herself as well as to him.

For a moment Blake continued to kiss her, his lips dropping to the curve of her breast where the weakened buttons of her blouse allowed him free passage.

"No, Blake, please." She began to twist, panic starting to enter her voice. She couldn't let him continue! *She* couldn't continue! Because if either of them did she would be completely lost! She wanted his touch . . . she wanted the feel of him, she wanted to be possessed by him so badly it was a pain throbbing deep within her. Yet not everything a person wanted was good for them—and she knew with a certainty, that he was not. That he could so easily slip through her barriers and make her forget all her firmly held resolves terrified her—now more than ever.

Her fear must have gotten through to him because suddenly all outward movement stopped and, after a breathless second passed, he raised his head to look at her. Cindy saw the glazed passion in his brown eyes and the need that echoed her own written on his face. He was looking at her as if he were unsure of what he had heard.

Cindy twisted once again. It was a signal he could not misinterpret.

"What is it?" he asked roughly. "What's wrong?"

Cindy was successful in putting a little distance between them. She sat up and moved a few inches away, running a shaking hand over her hair, feeling the bits of leaves and twigs, and absently trying to remove them.

She avoided looking directly into his eyes. "I wanted to stop," she whispered tightly.

Her words fell into a silence. She looked everywhere but at him. He knew she had enjoyed what had come to pass, had almost asked for it each step along the way.

Finally he sat up as well and raked a hand through his hair. It was steady, rock steady.

"All right. If you want to stop, we stop."

Those words were so different from what Cindy would ordinarily have expected to hear. It was getting a little tiresome comparing Blake to David—she seemed to be constantly doing it—but it was only human when two such complete opposites vied for attention in her life, one in memory, the other in the present. But David would never have reacted in that way. Whenever she had tried to put him off when he was determined to take her, he had behaved badly, like a spoiled baby. He had ranted and raved about her lack of response, and almost always bullied her into submission. And yet Blake, whom she had encouraged, was accepting her withdrawal without trying in any way to make her change her mind.

Miserably Cindy glanced at him only to pull her eyes away before speaking. "I'm sorry. I just . . ."

"You don't have to explain."

"But I—"

"Cindy," he interrupted firmly, "I want you to trust me. If it doesn't feel right for you, I don't want to go on. I'm not an animal. I can control myself. I want to please you, Cindy. Lovemaking isn't right unless both people enjoy it."

Once again Cindy was without a reply. With more and more frequency she was finding that Blake was a kind of man she had never encountered before. Was it possible that he was real?

What could have been a time of awkwardness between them was not. And Blake was responsible for that as well. He levered himself up to his feet and extended a hand to pull Cindy up. He gave an encouraging smile when she hesitated.

"Come on," he mocked gently. "Last one to the cabin's a rotten egg."

Unbelievably Cindy started to laugh. She would never have thought it possible, but she did. And when Blake, true to his challenge, started to run, so did she. They arrived at the front door at almost the same exact instant, with Blake only a little ahead.

He had allowed her to finish a close second. His long legs could make a mockery of her shorter ones in a real race—she knew that—but the twinkling enjoyment in his eyes and the wide smile that showed his happiness kept her from voicing her suspicions.

CHAPTER NINE

Much to Cindy's surprise she slept well that night. She had been afraid that with the long nap that had lasted far into the afternoon and the afternoon's disturbing events, rest would be illusive. But fact turned out different. She awoke the next morning totally refreshed, and even Blake's morning greeting combined with his news that they were leaving soon for his sister's house could not dampen her spirit of optimism. Why she should so suddenly become optimistic, she didn't know. It had been years since she had felt quite so carefree but that was the way she felt. And she wasn't about to fight it. She was young, she was alive, and this was a new day.

When Blake produced a strange car, seemingly from thin air, and ushered her into it—Prince as well—Cindy couldn't help making the wry observation, "Never let it be said you're a boring man. Where did you hide this—up your sleeve?"

Blake gave a short laugh and glanced at her, pausing after having shifted gears. "No, nothing quite so exotic. Try a garage." And at her questioning look. "It's just out of sight over that way." He motioned vaguely with his right hand. "One of Dad's peccadilloes was that he didn't want anything to remind him of the outside world—no cars in sight, no telephones, no televisions. To him they were all mind-destroyers taking away a man's image of himself. Air-conditioning he tolerated, indoor plumbing my mother insisted on. Electricity . . . well, he wasn't that much of a fanatic. But in every other way, he wanted a simpler life. And I can't say that I disagreed then, or do now."

Cindy relaxed thoughtfully in her seat. No, she couldn't say that she disagreed either. Somehow, from what she had come to know and appreciate, that ideology was not in the least sacrilegious. In fact, the opposite would be true. Not having a telephone had, in the beginning, been a problem when she had wanted to report Blake to the police. And the absence of a television was an adjustment that had to be made, not that she watched it that much when she was at home by herself. In reality the loss had been painless and she had not missed what had come to be necessities in most people's lives.

The atmosphere in the car was pleasant as they drove into the city. Prince, taking up most of the back seat, finally stopped getting excited as each car passed on the freeway and Blake's frame of mind seemed to echo her own sunny tone.

Cindy didn't allow herself to think too deeply. If she did, she might wonder at her changed attitude, at her curious excitement in accompanying Blake to a family party, at her practical erasure from her mind of his contention to his sister that they were engaged. If she let herself dwell on questioning those ideas, she would become confused and depressed. And she wanted to be neither. Something had happened to her yesterday, had possibly been sneaking up on her for several days. She didn't have a name for it yet, but she was happy. For the first time in a long time, she was really and truly happy.

Not just telling herself that she was. And she didn't want to lose it.

Veronica's home was in a nicely set-up area just a little north and west of the main growth of Houston. It was a large Tudor-style house, two stories and rambling with a comfortable elegance that fairly cried out its owners' status.

Veronica came rushing out of her front door as soon as the sleek Pontiac Trans Am drew to a stop.

"Blake! Oh, I'm so glad you came early." Veronica turned to include Cindy. "You too, Cindy!"

Cindy smiled a little nervously. It was all coming back. But Blake's sister's mind was obviously on something else and soon the feeling passed.

Veronica hurried over to grasp her brother's arm. "Blake, please. I need your help. Everything else is under control, but I've been going crazy about the florist. Somehow—don't ask me how—our order's been confused. Would you go over and talk to them? Please?"

Blake gave a long-suffering sigh and murmured as if to himself, "I knew I should have stayed away until time for the party—"

"Please!"

"Can we at least come in to get a drink of water?" His teasing question chased away any hint of displeasure.

"Of course." Veronica's face was suddenly lighted by a smile, relief at having the burden shifted to other shoulders visibly having taken effect. "More than one if you like."

"You're so very kind."

"And so are you."

Brother and sister gazed at each other fondly, the veneer of sophisticated rivalry reflecting a much deeper emotion.

Blake threw an arm about Veronica's shoulders and came around the car to do likewise to Cindy. When he started to turn away with the intention of accompanying them to the front door, an aggrieved *woof* drew him up short.

"Good grief, I forgot Prince," he exclaimed ruefully.

All eyes turned to the mastiff who sat staring back expectantly.

"You brought that monster?" Veronica breathed the question with a mixture of amusement and dismay.

"I couldn't very well leave him at the cabin," Blake returned innocently.

"But where are we going to put him?" his sister wailed in a voice Cindy at once sympathized with.

To Blake the answer was simple. "In the backyard with Sophie."

"With Sophie . . ."

"Sure. She won't mind."

"But she's just a little poodle! He might step on her by accident and kill her!"

Blake disagreed. "Prince wouldn't do anything like that. He's a gentleman."

"Which is more than I can say about a certain someone I know!"

Cindy couldn't help it; she gave a short laugh which caused Blake to fix her with a mock outraged stare, one eyebrow rising high.

"Are you trying to tell me you agree? What have I ever done to you?"

Cindy met his challenge. "What haven't you done is more the case. Would you care for a list in alphabetical order?"

Veronica observed this exchange and commented, her brown eyes, so similar to Blake's, twinkling. "So you haven't won out yet, brother mine. What's the matter? Is your technique slipping?"

Blake held Cindy's eyes for several seconds before purposely changing the subject. "Which florist is it you're having trouble with?"

Veronica took the hint and answered his question. Blake nodded as he moved away to release Prince.

"We'll take care of it," he promised.

And they did. Blake made efficient work of getting Prince settled—Sophie not minding his presence nearly as much as her owner seemed to. Veronica then took Cindy to a spare bedroom and instructed her where she could hang the dress she had brought for the party. And inside of fifteen minutes they were on their way again. Blake had not offered her the option of staying, and Cindy had not even thought about it herself since being with Blake now seemed so natural.

The mixup at the florist's was a simple matter, the confusion having been well on the road to repair even before they arrived. So, with some extra time available, Blake suggested that they go to a nearby shopping mall where he wanted to find a present for his mother.

"I haven't thought much about what to get her. But it seems I'm always shopping for some present or other. In our family we use any excuse as a chance to give one another gifts. St. Patrick's Day, April Fool's Day, the Fourth of July. It doesn't matter to us."

Cindy nodded, not really needing this confirmation. She had already sensed as much. Possibly the closeness of his family was the reason Blake was the way he was. With that kind of support all his life, how could he be anything but well adjusted? He certainly had no problem with his image. He didn't worry that for him to be a children's writer could be thought of as not being very macho in some people's eyes. He simply didn't care. To him, the people who had a problem with that were the ones with a problem. And Cindy couldn't help but applaud that attitude.

The next hour was spent at a leisurely pace. Blake asked her opinion of every item he considered, his right arm angled snugly along her back, his hand at her ribs. The warm fingers just under and to the side of her breast made it impossible not to be aware of him. Just as she was not unaware of the covert and not so covert looks he received from some of the women they passed. It was midday Monday and many of them were from offices surrounding the shopping complex. Cindy experienced a surge of possession. Blake was with *her.* He *wanted* to be with her. He had gone to great lengths just to have her near. He had even said he wanted to marry her!

At that she pulled herself up short. God! What was she thinking? She had to take hold of herself! She couldn't continue that line of thought. Not long ago she had been one of those women from the nearby offices, and, at the end of the week, she would be again. She couldn't let herself lose control in this way.

While Blake was taking a second look at a ring a jeweler was showing him, Cindy slipped away, pretending interest in some necklaces in a showcase farther away. When she got to the entryway, she kept on going until she stood in front of the window display of a shop next door. She stayed there, unseeing, unaware, not really noticing the people rushing by or even where she was. Only one thing filled her mind: She could escape, do what she had wanted to do from the beginning, but her feet refused to carry her. They remained firmly entrenched on the spot where she was and she remained there until Blake came to stand close to her side.

She chanced a quick glance at his profile. It could have been her imagination, but he seemed a little pale. Had he thought she might take advantage of this chance as well?

Woodenly Cindy turned back to the window and stared at an array of antique Japanese fans. Her breathing was a little shallow. She could hear that Blake's was as well.

Finally he broke the silence that had stretched between them by saying, "I decided on the ring." His words were prosaic, everyday. She knew they weren't what he really wanted to say.

"Good."

That wasn't what she wanted to say either. She wanted to yell, to scream, to do something that would break this spell he seemed to have cast over her. And if she couldn't do that, ridiculous as it seemed, she wanted to kiss him. Right here, right now. She wanted to press her body to his and move against him until they both forgot modesty, decency. She wanted him. She wanted his touch, wanted to feel the smoothness of his bronze skin against her own, wanted the drugging intensity of his mouth on hers. She wanted him totally, completely, ached for his possession. Yet she remained still, just as he did. And when at last they moved away from the window, Blake was careful not to touch her.

Cindy was in a strange, unsettled mood as she dressed for the party that evening. She wanted to be here; she didn't want to be here. She wanted to be with Blake; she didn't want to be with Blake. She wanted to meet more of his family, especially his mother, but was afraid to meet them. She felt a fraud, a pretender. Not once since they had arrived had Blake mentioned that she was any more to him than a friend. But was she even that? Friendships had always taken her a long time to solidify. How long had she known Blake? Two weeks? And not really even all of that time. But she knew so much about him. Living together in the cabin had shown her more than most people would learn about another person in a year. She knew he was strong, yet at the same time gentle. He was virile; he could excite her unwilling body with one look, much less a touch, yet he didn't take advantage of her weakness when her sense of reason forced her to stop. He was kind, thoughtful; he loved and was loved by his family. Rarely had she seen him angry, and when he was, he was able to contain it. She had never even seen him drink. He had a wonderful sense of humor, even if it was a little offbeat sometimes. He was everything she had always wanted in a man. And yet, in some way, for some reason, she was frightened of him. Frightened to let herself come too close to liking him. He fascinated her. Yes, that was what it was, fascination. He was unique, a man different from all the others she had known. Possibly if she tried to look upon him as some kind of experiment—a fluke of genetics—she would be able to remain detached.

A light tap on the door brought Cindy from her troubled thoughts. Before she had time to call a reply, Blake pushed his head inside.

"Are you decent?" he asked, his cinnamon eyes alive with good humor.

Out the window went Cindy's ideas of an experiment. How anyone could think of so vibrant a man with detachment, as if he were a piece of scientific evidence to be picked up and examined at will . . .

A nervous quiver ran over her, but she hid it by retorting, "A lot of good it would do me if I weren't. You're already in."

Blake pushed the door farther open and came entirely inside the room. He too had changed for the party. A dark blue suit with a pastel blue shirt and striped tie complemented his good looks. But, then, he looked good in everything he chose to wear. If he had chosen to dress in his usual attire of faded jeans and a comfortably worn shirt, he would still manage to make every woman's heart throb at a distance of ten miles. And Cindy was not immune.

"Do you need something?" she was forced to ask, her voice tightening as he continued to look at her while she went through the motions of putting the finishing touches to her hair.

Her inquiry seemed to amuse him. "That's a loaded question if I ever heard one. Do you really want me to answer?"

Irritation at her own stupidity in laying herself open made her snap. "No, I have a pretty good imagination—and with you, there's only one subject to choose from." She knew the accusation was unfair, but couldn't seem to stop herself.

Blake let the acidity of her reply roll off him. "Would you really prefer it if I stopped paying attention to you, Cindy?"

"It might make a nice change." She hated to sound so shrewish but it was the only way she had of protecting herself; he had such a powerful effect over her.

He moved until he was standing close behind her, one hand coming out to cup the skin at her throat.

"Are you very sure?"

The husky murmur as his mouth came down to touch the curve of her ear made Cindy unsure of anything. The long fingers carefully tightened their hold, a mild assurance that she would not pull away.

The warmth of his body acted as a magnet and she felt herself being drawn against him.

Blake's lips slipped from her ear to the side of her neck, nuzzling the soft skin, brushing against it with mesmerizing effect.

"I want to love you again, Cindy," he whispered softly, causing a piercing shaft of electricity to shoot through her as his mouth continued its plundering trail. "I have to."

Cindy's head dropped back to allow him more freedom. She strained up on her toes to help equalize the difference in their heights and blissful seconds passed as their lovemaking continued. Blake transferred his hand to her waist and brought the other up to fondle the rounded swell of her breast as she reveled in his touch.

When he twisted her head to kiss her mouth, she reacted hungrily, clinging to him, her hands slipping beneath his jacket to move over the firm muscles of his back, the sweet sensual ecstasy almost too much for her.

Then before she even knew they had moved, they were lying across the bed, Blake's long length pressed tightly to hers.

Cindy made a small sound that might have been a protest but Blake's lips prevented any words from being born, and soon she was once again too entrapped in his sensual spell even to think.

His experienced hands moved with magical precision over her body, using the knowledge he had gained in the past to bring her closer to the celebration of their mutual desire.

Cindy's heartbeat was erratic as the warmth and need of his body was communicated unmistakingly to hers. Her fingers were trembling as they caressed the sides of his neck and wandered into his thick chestnut hair . . .

Blake gave a groan of satisfaction as his pleasure surged . . .

It took the jarring impact of another knock on her door to bring them back from the depths of their rapture.

They both became still, waiting, unsure if the sound had been real or a part of their imagination. Cindy's deep violet eyes were held by Blake's heated brown ones.

The knocking came again. "Cindy? Are you in there? Is Blake with you?" Veronica called, her questions tinged with the slightest amount of impatience.

Blake gave a muttered curse of frustration. But as he slowly released Cindy from his arms, and rose from the bed, his answer was light and mocking. "Yes, Ronnie. Blake is with Cindy."

Cindy was hurriedly trying to straighten her bodice, her complexion a high shade of pink. This wasn't the first time Veronica had interrupted them—only the last time she had been a few minutes too late, or too early, depending upon your point of view. But this time, thank the Lord, her arrival was timed just right.

"Oh—" Veronica's reply was a little nonplussed. Then she recovered. "I'm sorry. I didn't mean to intrude, but nearly everyone is here and Ted will be arriving soon with Mom. I thought you might like to come down . . . be there when Mom . . ." Her voice trailed away.

Blake exhaled a long breath and looked at Cindy, his brown eyes glittering with a mixture of suppressed desire and irony.

Cindy looked away; she didn't want to meet his gaze. She could sense the small frown that descended on his brow as he continued to watch her. His puzzlement was evident when he promised his sister, "We'll be right there, Ronnie."

"Okay," she replied. Then, as if she couldn't resist, she

gaily intoned as she walked away from the door, "I hope you two haven't been doing anything I wouldn't do . . ."

Blake gave a short laugh and shook his head. "Brat. She hasn't changed since she was two—"

The room was still after that comment and Cindy was unable to break the silence. She picked up the brush from where it had fallen to the floor and again started to move it through her hair. All the while she could feel Blake's eyes boring into her.

"What's the matter, Cindy?" he asked softly, his words filled with concern.

"Nothing," she answered, tension making her strokes choppy.

Blake took a step toward her but stopped when she pulled sharply away. His lips thinned.

"Well, something as sure as hell is! A minute ago you seemed in a remarkably different mood."

"I've changed my mind."

"I don't believe you really know your mind." He was quick to retaliate.

The truth of that statement was unassailable.

"Possibly not."

"Cindy, look at me," Blake directed.

Cindy refused. He took another step forward and this time raised her chin with his fingers, forcing her to meet the steady expression in his brown gaze.

"If there was one thing I never thought of you, it's that you were a coward. But now I'm beginning to wonder." He gave her chin a little shake. "Come on, Cindy. I can't do this all alone! You've got to help—do your part. This stupid aversion you have to admitting the truth is only making both of us miserable. I love you, Cindy. I have from the first second I set eyes on you. I know that sounds trite and ridiculous, but it's true. And nothing that has happened since has changed my mind. I love you. I want to marry you. I'd like to be able to go downstairs right this very minute and tell everyone that we're engaged—officially engaged."

He paused, waiting for her to comment. And when she didn't, he searched her frozen expression, looking for some spark of feeling. But Cindy refused to allow anything to show. On the outside she was as cold and hard as steel, but inside he was scaring her to death. She didn't want him to love her! Until he said those words she could pretend that he was playing with her, as if in some kind of childish amusement. Now she couldn't dissemble any longer, and she didn't know what to do!

Blake was not yet ready to relinquish his stand. "I refuse to believe that what's happened between us is merely physical!"

"Believe what you want," Cindy returned from between stiff lips.

A little flare of anger lighted the dark cinnamon of Blake's eyes. "No!"

Cindy gave a little shrug, her body wanting to do nothing more than collapse into a frenzy of shivering, but it was being held in check by her determination not to give in.

His anger increased as did the strength of his hold on her chin. However, when he saw her flinch, he immediately released his grip.

A muttered, "I'm sorry if I hurt you," followed.

Tears in her violet eyes, Cindy nodded. She could say nothing, her insides felt as if they had been ripped apart.

Blake remained unmoving for several more seconds then crossed jerkily to the door. "I'll wait five minutes then I'm going down."

Still Cindy made no reply and he left the room, his back ramrod straight, his head forced high.

After that encounter, the party lost most of its luster for Cindy. Everyone else seemed happy though—the myriad relatives talking at breakneck pace, as if they hadn't seen one another in a long time, waiting for the appearance of the woman who had no idea that they were there.

Cindy stayed out of the way as much as she could, Blake having wordlessly brought her downstairs then disappeared after depositing her in a chair next to one of his aunts.

The aunt had done nothing but praise her nephew; he was a saint to hear her describe him. No one could find a better husband. Cindy had listened and wanted to scream. And the feeling only increased as one after another of his relatives came to meet her, each questioning in his own way the relationship between them. *Friends, just friends,* she had answered repeatedly, until she thought the words were going to be imprinted in her brain for the rest of her life.

She was almost to the point of seeking a way to flee when Veronica hurried from one room to the other, calling out in a stage whisper for everyone to be quiet, that her husband's car had just come to a stop in the drive.

After that fact became known, a silence descended over the house. Cindy waited as well, her nerves strung high, but not for the same reason. She let her eyes take in the room, noticing for the first time the flowers positioned strategically throughout.

Her gaze went from examining the room to searching among the people. Short, tall, wide, thin, old, young, in between, dressed well, dressed poorly, in good taste and bad. They were a mishmash, like any other crowd. But they had one thing in common, the pleasantness of their expressions. And if one or two looked worried or out of sorts, from the lines that marked their faces she could sense that the upset was only temporary.

Finally her search was rewarded. Blake was standing beside his sister on the far side of the room, waiting, it seemed for their mother to come in. But his eyes were on her. Cindy was caught and held. He was sending her a message and she was receiving it. *Don't be a coward,* he was challenging. *Come over to me—stand by me. Let yourself do it!*

It took a tremendous amount of effort, but Cindy succeeded in jerking her eyes away. By doing so she was conceding his challenge; she knew it. But maybe she was a coward. Wasn't there some saying about cowards living longer? Maybe that was what she needed. Time to think. Everything was too rushed, so pressured now.

The front door opened and a woman's voice could be heard protesting. "Ted, I don't know why you insisted on doing this. I can see the new curtains any time. I didn't really want to get out today . . ."

Then the woman appeared. If Cindy had been asked to choose Blake's mother, she would never have picked the correct one. She was small, not much larger than herself; her hair was a dull shade of brownish-gray, her face, though not plain, was definitely not anywhere near the sculptured beauty of her children's. The woman stopped and looked at the roomful of people in amazement. Silently the question What? formed on her lips. Then she looked at Veronica and Blake and she knew.

Veronica waited no longer. She flew across the few steps that separated them and enveloped her mother in a loving embrace. "Happy Anniversary, love."

Blake then took his sister's place. He bent to take his mother in his arms and, as he did, the woman's shocked expression dissolved into a mist of tears. Soon everyone was giving their greetings and converging on the surprised woman.

Cindy wasn't aware of when Blake came to stand beside her, so she gave a small start when he prompted softly, "Come meet my mother." She allowed him to guide her across the room.

When she was introduced, Cindy was aware of being the center of the large group's attention. She cringed when she thought Blake would continue the charade and name her as his fiancée, but her worry was for nothing. Neither he nor Veronica said anything.

On closer inspection Blake's mother was not any more spectacular than she had looked from across the room, except for her eyes. They were a soft dove gray, alive with love and tears. Kindness and tenderness were the windows of this one particular woman's soul, and from the gracious hello she extended, Cindy felt warmed, while at the same time sensing a great sadness.

With very little effort she was then able to glide back into the crowd and watch from a seat in an out-of-the-way chair as gifts were presented and opened. Numerous times she heard Blake's father's name mentioned. At first it was regretfully, then, essential to healing, in fond remembrance. Humorous stories circulated and people laughed, even Blake's mother, although her laughter was a little strained.

Through all of this Cindy remained alone, forgotten, which was exactly what she wanted, since she wasn't really a part of the family.

She had to participate in the dinner that followed though, and since she was seated next to Blake, her already-reduced appetite was all the more nonexistent. He noticed that she was eating very little, but made no comment, contenting himself to talk with a cousin who was seated across from them. Cindy pretended to listen, but the words blurred. She was just existing. Almost drifting. She didn't know what was the matter with her, why everything seemed to be happening to a stranger, as if she were just a shell taking up space and talking only when compelled to do so.

Blake had said he loved her.

Was this entire experience nothing more than a dream—and a bad one at that? From the corner of her eye she observed Blake as he forked a tender piece of chicken and brought it upward to his mouth. He had kissed her, told her he wanted her, told her he loved her, and then said he wanted to marry her. God! Why didn't it seem real? Was it because she was afraid? But of what? Just because a man says he loves and wants to marry you, it didn't mean that you had to respond positively. Or even to respond. He said he didn't believe it was just a sexual attraction between them. Did she? Damn, she was so confused! Would this party never end? She was past wanting to go back to the quietness of the cabin. Now she was longing to be there. She wanted peace, quiet. She had to think.

After the meal she moved quietly with the crowd into a room toward the back of the house in which the furniture had been cleared. She started when a soft featherlike touch on her arm drew her attention.

It was Veronica. But the attention was not for herself. With tears gathering in her eyes, she pointed to the couple who, at that moment, were the only people occupying the center of the cleared area. It was Blake and his mother; they were dancing to the melancholy strains of a Gershwin tune. Cindy's ears had been deaf to the music in the beginning, but as she watched, the sound became more clear—*Someone to Watch over Me.* The lyrics were sung by a woman whose voice was fraught with emotion, making even the most hardened listener feel the depths of her need.

"That was my parents' favorite song," Veronica whispered, her voice tight, tears building. "Each year, from the time we were babies, whether they celebrated their anniversary with a party or not, my father would always put that old record on and dance with my mother. It was a kind of ritual between them. He once told me their first date had been to a movie that used that song as a theme throughout. He said he fell in love with Mom right then and that she did with him too. They were married a few weeks later."

The song was continuing as Blake held his mother close, moving slowly to the music. Veronica continued. "I'm glad Blake's dancing with her now—it's only right. He looks so much like Dad did when he was young."

Cindy could not take her eyes away from the couple. Blake's mother had her eyes closed, but accumulated tears could be seen hovering on her lashes.

An empathetic pain struck her heart. To have loved and been loved to such a degree . . . She had never experienced such a love or seen one. In fact she had never been in a family situation where there was so much caring. Her eyes followed Blake, riveted to the way he had to hunch a little to accommodate his mother's small stature—just as he did with her. How his chestnut head was bent protectively. How his lean strong body was giving strength and courage to the woman he held close, substituting in his own way, for the loss she had suffered.

When the dance finally came to an end, Cindy had to blink quickly to disperse the tears that had gathered. And she wasn't the only one. Veronica, next to her, was wiping her cheeks and sniffing.

But there was more yet to come. Blake's mother tiptoed painfully up to give a short kiss to her son's tanned cheek. And Blake, returning the salute, held his mother's clasped hands in his.

Only the sounds of more music broke the hushed spell that had fallen over the people, each touched by the display of healing tenderness exhibited before them. And soon a few other couples ventured out to dance, letting Blake lead his mother away. They came to where Veronica and Cindy were positioned.

Blake's mother was smiling a watery smile, which had the quality of beauty. Tears were still brightening her gray eyes and, for a few seconds, the illusion of youth conjured from the past remained. But mixed with it was sadness although Cindy could see that it had lessened in degree. Veronica had succeeded in her plan.

Cindy moved a step backward, not wanting to intrude in this private family moment. But Blake saw her movement and halted her with a glance.

Cindy couldn't pull her eyes away. A tenseness was about him. This time she couldn't interpret the message in his eyes, but she had no trouble understanding, at last, what was in her own heart. And the knowledge petrified her.

From the first he had annoyed her, intrigued her, infuriated her, fascinated her, frightened her. She had been drawn, yet at the same time was repelled. She hadn't wanted to become attracted to any man ever again! She had attained independence and needed no one! But did love ever truly listen?

As she thought the word, her mind mutinied. No! She couldn't love him! If she allowed that to happen, she would make herself vulnerable again—open to all the old hurt.

She would not let herself love him!

She would not!

Prince was the only occupant of the car who was at ease during the drive back to the cabin. He was spread out on the back seat sound asleep. Of the two humans, one was withdrawn, having been since leaving his sister's, and the other was preoccupied with the construction of a wall of ice, one that would withstand even an assault from within.

The trip seemed to be accomplished in record time, so wrapped up was each in their own thoughts. Cindy had to make herself come back to awareness when the Trans Am rolled to a stop beside her Datsun. She flicked a quick glance toward Blake, although the darkness of the night did not allow her much vision. Yet she was aware of him, and, as a reaction, retracted even farther away in her seat.

That movement brought Blake from his reverie. His head swiveled toward her, and she could feel the touch of his eyes.

"You're very quiet," he whispered softly.

A tremble went through Cindy, but she quickly subdued it. "You haven't been very talkative yourself," she returned.

His attention remained upon her through the inky blackness. For several minutes he just continued to look at her and she began to wonder if he had the eyes of a night predator and was able to see her clearly. She moved uncomfortably in her seat, wanting to leave but being kept there as if by some invisible force.

Finally he sighed and agreed, "No."

Another silence fell between them. Then he asked, "Have you thought about what I told you?"

A knot of tension curled in her stomach. She had

thought about little else—as well as her own unwanted discovery!

"Yes." The word was terse; she was relieved.

"And?"

"And what?"

Irritation seemed to break in him. "Stop playing stupid, Cindy! You know what I'm talking about. I want to marry you!"

"Is anything else new?" she mocked, glad of the darkness. "You've been telling me that from the first day I met you."

"Is that all you have to say?" he demanded.

She could feel his frustration but hardened herself to it. In a voice that left little hope she returned levelly, "I want the keys to my car, Blake."

She heard his quick intake of breath and experienced the first attack on her citadel.

"Doesn't it matter to you that I love you?" he asked.

She quickly repaired the damage of the first assault and braced for the next.

"No."

"Why?"

"Because I didn't ask for your love."

Blake leaned toward her, his hands coming out to grasp her shoulders and turn her toward him. Unconsciously they ground into her flesh.

"I know you're attracted to me—"

"Of course," she interrupted. "Aren't most women?"

She could feel his tight smile.

"I'm only interested in one right now."

"And she's not interested in you. I'm bored with acting as a toy in your little game, Blake. I want to go home."

"I've told you before, it's no game."

"To me it is."

His fingers tightened even more, but Cindy knew he was still unaware of it. She faced him bravely, a barely discernible shadow who refused to cower away. She knew in order to free herself she had to convince him. Fear drove her onward.

"You're really beginning to leave me a little cold, Blake. Hasn't anyone ever turned you down before and meant it?"

She could feel the anger that had been building in him reach fever pitch. He disregarded entirely the last part of her question and concentrated on the first. Possibly he had not even heard beyond her first sentence.

"Leave you cold." He gave a hard laugh. "Like hell I leave you cold!" He jerked her toward him.

Physically Cindy was pulled off balance, but mentally she was still waging war and had no intention of losing.

His lips were almost touching hers when she hissed angrily, "You're just like all the rest, aren't you, Blake? If a woman won't give you what you want, take it. Isn't that the way it goes? Just exactly like my ex-husband—but at least he had the memory of my love, and the fact of it, until he killed it with his boorishness."

If she had withdrawn a knife and cut deeply into his vital organs, she could not have wounded Blake more. A violent shudder passed over him and the grip of his fingers instantly lessened. Even in the darkness she could sense the paleness of his face and his sick look of revulsion.

Within the second he had completely released her and was pushing open his door. Prince, starting awake, jumped between the seats and hurried after his master's retreating form, leaving Cindy alone and trembling as she pondered the bitterness of her victory.

CHAPTER TEN

How long Cindy remained sitting in the car she was never to know. Eons could have passed and she would have been unaware. She had hurt him—she had hurt him terribly. She knew he was nothing like David. She wanted to go to him, tell him. But she stayed where she was. She couldn't do that. She had to keep a distance between them for her own survival.

Love had played a dirty trick on her. It wasn't something she had wanted. In fact she had actively resisted, vehemently resisted. And she was going to continue to do so. If a person could fall into love, certainly they could fall out. And that was exactly what she was going to do.

If she could get away from Blake, away from his influence, then maybe she could put him from her mind and forget him.

She had done a pretty good job with David. She had no idea where he was now and didn't really care. Just so long as he stayed far away from her. If only she could put the same kind of distance between herself and Blake . . .

With a slow stiff movement Cindy reached for the door release and stepped out of the car. Then, after a moment of hesitation, she began to move toward the cabin. Where Blake and Prince were she could only guess.

But she wasn't to remain in ignorance for long. As she

approached the porch, a tall lean figure emerged from the shadows and caused her heart to go into a thundering pace, as if it were trying to dislodge itself from her chest by way of her throat. Her hand reached out to one of the rough wooden beams for support.

Blake said nothing as he bent to unlock the cabin door. When this was done, he stepped aside to let her enter first.

Cindy moved quickly inside, Prince at her heels. The big dog lumbered over to his favorite spot before the fireplace and laid down to complete his interrupted rest.

Blake shut the door behind them and wordlessly brushed past without even looking at her.

She stared after his departing back, her violet eyes shadowed. She watched as he walked stiffly toward the hall then listened as the door to his room shut with aching finality.

A deep, tremulous sigh passed through her lips and a haze of tears spurted to her eyes. These she quickly blinked away. She didn't have time for emotionalism. It was only a trap that would keep her here. And above all things, she had to get away!

She had come full circle. In the beginning she had wanted to escape, not fully understanding the reason why but instinctively knowing that she must; then the situation had gradually changed and in some confusion she had found herself no longer wanting to leave. Then had come the revelation, and now she knew she must leave again.

But her problem remained the same throughout. She still had no transportation without her car keys.

Cindy gave a frustrated glance toward the hall. Should she go once again and demand her property? Inwardly she cringed at the idea and silently answered her own question. No. It was too soon. Her defenses, though well built, were too new to withstand yet another siege. Not that

Blake seemed to be interested in offering any further persuasion.

Cindy jerked her thoughts away, the feeling of panic returning. See what happened when she was near him? Her emotions became so jumbled she didn't know whether she was up or down. She had to get away—the manner didn't matter any longer!

With quick, urgent steps Cindy hurried to her room and dragged her valises onto the bed, throwing in as many of her possessions as could easily fit. What was left behind she would replace. A toothbrush, her special facial soap, some bath powder. First thing tomorrow morning she was going to leave, and this time it didn't matter if she had to crawl. It would be day. No nighttime animals would be on the prowl.

She was in the process of shutting her last suitcase when the door was pushed open behind her. She whirled about, startled, her purple gaze wide.

Blake stood in the doorway. If at first she thought he might be intent on finishing what he had started outside—that renewed anger had replaced the suffering from her hurtful barb and he was ready to try to once again use force—she soon discovered her mistake.

His brown gaze took in the evidence of her determined departure, and for a split second a bleak look settled on his handsome features. But as quickly as it came it vanished, and she was left to wonder if she had imagined the desolate expression.

"It would be best if you'd wait until morning," he suggested flatly, the words those which one stranger would use to another.

"Yes," Cindy returned tightly. "I was."

Blake nodded and transferred his eyes to the scene his father had painted that hung on the bedroom wall. He was silent for a moment, then he said, "I made a mistake, Cindy." His glance came back to her in a lightning move. "I should never have tried to make you stay. It was foolish for me to think I could persuade you to care but I guess my only excuse is that I wanted you near me so much. I was so damned sure I could make you happy." He opened his fingers to show her the keys that were laying in his palm. "You'll probably need these."

For a time Cindy could only stare at them. Then, with fingers as cold as the metal they reached for, she plucked the keys lightly from his hand.

"Take care of yourself," his husky voice advised, before he turned and closed the door behind him.

The next morning she was free! And with each passing mile her Datsun ate up, the cabin was becoming farther and farther away. So why didn't she feel any better? She had accomplished what she wanted. She had her car, most of her pride, and she was away from the strong power of Blake's influence. Why did this sick feeling persist?

With a determined toss of her dark head, Cindy narrowed her eyes against the brightness of the rising sun and pressed down even harder on the accelerator. She was free. Free to again take up her life where it had been interrupted, free to come as she wanted, leave when she pleased.

Only physical freedom is much easier to gain than emotional, a fact Cindy was to learn the hard way over the next few days.

She had purposely stayed away from the agency, not wanting to have to explain to Marcy the reason why she was back so early in the week, and the days had dragged. Then Monday, on a job that should have been extremely interesting and stimulating, she was strangely lethargic.

For the next two weeks her life was like a giant rollercoaster ride; only the highs weren't very high and the lows were dreadful.

She couldn't get Blake out of her mind! And it was much, much worse than when she first met him. No matter what she did, where she went, or whom she was with, her thoughts were constantly centered upon him, the look of him, the feel of him near her, the sound of his voice. Everything that had happened at the cabin was replayed over and over in her mind. She even found herself missing Prince!

Finally one night, like a volcano about to explode, the emotional torment within Cindy became too much to bear. She was at home, having turned down a date on the pretext of a headache, not ready even yet to admit that it was not her head that was hurting. She tried to sleep but ended up tossing restlessly until her sheets looked like an army had bivouacked overnight before departing in a hurry. Restlessly she padded into her small kitchen and opened the refrigerator door. She had skipped supper that evening, not really feeling like food, but now, just to have something to do, she rummaged around until she found some luncheon meat, a boiled egg, and the two remaining pickles in the pickle jar. This she cradled in her arms and transported into her living room.

Normally Cindy watched very little television. It was a convenience used only on occasion. And she could never make herself get interested in old movies—not that they weren't good—it was just that she never seemed to have the time. Now she did. The hour was late, around two, if her bleary eyes had looked at the kitchen clock right, and there was nothing else to do.

She switched on the set and curled into a comfortable position on her couch. Immediately she found that she had tuned in during one of the long commercial breaks that peopled the airways late at night, so she trundled back into the kitchen for her forgotten drink.

With a little grunt of impatience she found that the Coke remaining in the refrigerator was only enough to splash about the bottom of her empty glass. She had to extract another from the pantry, but when she reached into the freezer for ice, she found both the trays were empty. Really! She fumed disgustedly to herself. Everything was falling apart in the apartment! She was so distracted, so absentminded. Since coming back from the cabin she had been like a woman under a spell, or in a dream. She had been . . .

Cindy stopped herself with a sharp "Damn!" Was she ever going to be able to live in peace? Even the most ordinary things reminded her of Blake! How much longer was it going to take?

Then suddenly her hands became still as she held an empty ice tray under running water. The strains of a familiar tune drifted in from the living room.

Cindy stood perfectly still, her eyes squeezed tightly shut as if hearing the lyrics had caused an actual aching within. *Someone who'll watch over me,* her mind echoed over again. Water filled the tray and ran wastefully down the drain.

With a crash Cindy dropped the tray and ran back into the living room, her hands dripping. No! It wasn't fair! Why that song? Why tonight of all nights?

As her disbelieving eyes stared at the screen, the television faded and was replaced by the sight of Blake dancing with his mother and images of so many other times when his caring and gentleness had been revealed to her. As the singer's voice mournfully cried out her need, Cindy slowly sank to the carpeted floor, her hands clenched into wet fists.

In spite of the distance she had put between herself and Blake, he could have been right in her living room this very minute! She could see the way his hair burned with reddish highlights in the sun, the way his cinnamon eyes glowed with happiness and laughter, the sadness he was not ashamed to show when they lost the battle for four little lives, the way he had bent his head protectively over his mother's, the way he looked at her when he wanted her, the husky quality of his voice.

A long, low moan started in Cindy's throat. God! Oh, God! She still loved him! She began to rock back and forth on her bent knees. She had never stopped loving him and probably never would! All the past two weeks had done was show her how truly lonely and empty her existence had been before she met him.

She loved him!

A trembling took hold of her body and she began to laugh—a high, shaky sound that was near a sob.

All right. She admitted it. But what was she going to do about it? What could she do about it?

She crossed her arms over her breasts and hugged her shoulders. She had to think.

She couldn't just go back to the cabin, walk in, and make her announcement, could she? What would Blake think? She gave another shaky laugh. He would probably decide that she was the crazy one this time! But if he loved her as he said he did . . .

Cindy jumped to her feet and juggled her proposed meal back into the kitchen and the safe coolness of the refrigerator.

Why not? Why not go back to the cabin? A deep excitement began to curl in the pit of her stomach.

The early hours of that morning seemed as if they would

never pass. Cindy spent most of them sitting in the middle of her bed, her arms wrapped about her updrawn knees, smiling in anticipation. She felt just like a teenager again . . . so brand new . . . love reborn. And this time she knew the difference. She had thought she loved David, but it was more an adolescent kind of love, an infatuation that did not stand up to the test of time or trouble. But with Blake . . . Cindy hugged her knees tighter. Blake was a man she respected, a man who knew the value of love and who found joy in giving and who gave of himself unstintingly to those he loved. Now that she had admitted it, she discovered just how deeply she felt. She loved him more than she thought possible.

That had been what she was afraid of all this time; that she did love him deeply, or had the capacity to. And now, looking back on the wasted time, she grew even more impatient. He had cared about her from the beginning, just like the story she'd been told about his father and mother, how they had fallen in love on their first date. Maybe in his family everyone believed in love at first sight!

She could hardly wait for the first light of day.

As Cindy drove along the deserted road that led to the cabin she remembered the first time she had traveled it. How uncomfortable she had felt in the forest, how disdainfully she had looked at the cabin. And now, here she was, hurrying as fast as she could, back to them, loving them, because they were a part of the man she loved.

When her car drew up in the clearing in front of the cabin, Cindy barely let the engine die before she was out and running up the pathway. She took the two steps onto the porch in one. Then before the space of a single breath she was rapping on the door and calling, "Blake! Blake, it's me. Cindy. I've got to talk to you, Blake!"

She knocked on the door for at least five minutes. She refused to believe that he was not there.

Finally, her voice strained and hoarse, she turned away, her spirit filled with dejection. He wasn't there. He had gone away.

Tears made the forest hazy as she looked out over it. Why? Why did she always do the wrong thing? First she jumped too quickly, then when a second chance at happiness appeared, she acted too slowly.

Cindy started to walk dejectedly back to her car. When she had first learned about him, Marcy had said he was visiting from California. Had he gone back? And if he had, how would she ever learn where to locate him there? Then her mind jumped to another idea. What if he wasn't gone? What if he was just out somewhere in the forest, possibly taking a long walk with Prince? How was she to know?

Then memory of another time came to her rescue. Blake had a car here, the black Pontiac Trans Am they had used to go to Veronica's! He had said it was kept in a garage which was hidden from sight of the cabin. What if she were to try to find it? If his car was still there, then so was he; and if it was not . . . well, she would deal with that eventuality when the time came. Right now, even just the possibility of his still being in the near vicinity lent hope to her spirit and she set off in the direction Blake had vaguely pointed toward when he had mentioned the garage.

To discover the sturdily built structure took Cindy some time. It was further away from the cabin than she had thought. But as a reward, she could see through a crack in the wide wooden door that the car was still safely within.

The small bird twittering in the tree above could be forgiven for staring curiously at the dark-haired woman below as she gave a joyful little yelp and then danced a fast jig in the fallen pine needles before turning to jog away from his sight.

With her soul full of renewed optimism, Cindy hurriedly retraced her steps, only this time she left out a few that had led her nowhere. Her return to the cabin took much less time.

However, as she drew near, her speed decreased and her trepidation increased. She wanted him to have returned, and yet, in one way, she didn't. She wasn't sure how to begin. Just because *she* wanted the chance to talk with him, would *he* be willing to listen?

Her knees were shaking from both exertion and nervousness as she mounted the porch steps once again. She had to swallow hard to retain her nerve. This time her tap on the wooden door was more sedate while excitement, dread, and a physical ache, all struggled for prevalence in her emotions.

When she heard the sound of footsteps on the other side, her heart gave a quick leap. He was here!

The door swept open and Blake narrowed his eyes against the glare. His expression was none too friendly.

"Look, Ronnie," he complained, "I don't want to be bothered . . ." The words trailed away into nothingness as he saw that the person without was definitely not his sister. "Cindy?" Her name was spoken almost disbelievingly.

Cindy had a hard time keeping from throwing herself into his arms. But uncertainty at how he would take the action stopped her.

"Hi," she returned and thought, *Stupid! Stupid! Stupid! How completely inane! Why don't I complete the absurdity by commenting on how hot the weather has been lately!*

Blake stepped aside after a stunned moment and made way for her to come inside.

Cindy wondered how he couldn't hear her bones rattling. She was trembling from head to foot.

Greeting Prince, who had come at a fast trot on hearing her voice, helped a little to cover the strained uneasiness between them. But she couldn't pet the dog forever—not when she really wanted to pet his master, if he would let her. Cindy looked up, her violet eyes a beautiful contrast to her dark hair.

She held Blake's suddenly wary gaze for only a short moment before looking around the cabin. "Did you ever finish that manuscript?"

"What manuscript?"

"The one I was typing before I . . ."

Blake shrugged when she didn't complete the sentence. "No, but I did get the revisions done."

"Oh." Cindy shifted position, wishing she had worn jeans instead of the peasant dress, so that she would have somewhere to put her hands.

"What brings you back?" Blake asked at last when it seemed she had nothing more to say.

Should she tell him? Cindy decided to wait and test the water a little more. She didn't want to bare her soul and find out that he had changed his mind. The humiliation, not to mention the despair, would be too great.

"I was in the neighborhood . . ."

A little of Blake's reserve melted. "So you thought you'd stop by. It's unbelievable how many people find themselves in that situation."

Cindy's cheeks reddened when she remembered the last time words similar to those had been used. Possibly her unconscious had remembered. It had been when Veronica had first interrupted them, after they had made love.

Cindy moved about the room, settling at a position by the typewriter. "Would you like some help?"

Blake eyed her suspiciously. "What will it cost me?"

Everything you've got? Cindy smiled to herself. Out loud she said, "It's free. I'm offering."

With easy strides Blake erased the distance between them and stood beside the desk as well. His cinnamon eyes examined her closely before he asked, his voice huskier than usual, "Just what kind of services are you offering?"

Cindy took a deep breath, nearly lost in the warm light she could see was beginning to dawn in his gaze. She decided to chance it.

"Myself . . . for life." At Blake's quickly indrawn breath she continued, "If you still want me—"

"Want you?" Blake repeated incredulously, then demanded, "Did Adam want Eve? Did Antony want Cleopatra? Did Romeo want Juliet?"

Cindy began to giggle, her nervousness escaping.

Blake didn't let her have a chance to make a reply. He swooped and gathered her into his arms.

"You are serious," he prodded, holding her tightly against him.

Her eyes shining Cindy replied, "Never more serious in my life!"

Cindy felt the tremor that shook his lean hard body.

"You won't change your mind?"

"No."

"You're positive?"

Cindy became impatient. Her body was on fire and he was talking! "Blake, if you don't hurry up and kiss me—"

Blake didn't give her the opportunity to finish that sentence. Very effectively he halted the motion of her lips with his.

Cindy put everything she had into that kiss—all her love, all her need. She wanted nothing more in the world than what she had right here—Blake in her arms, loving her, and the knowledge that he would go on loving her, just as she would him.

When at last their lips broke apart, Blake's breathing was ragged. "Woman, have I ever told you that I love you?" His warm brown eyes were vibrant with emotion.

"I believe you did once." Cindy kept her fingers firmly clasped behind his neck, enjoying the way her body was molded to the hard line of his.

Blake's hands lovingly caressed her waist and hips. "You didn't believe me."

"I was afraid to believe you," she corrected.

Blake looked at her in surprise. "Why?" he asked simply.

"Because I was beginning to care for you too."

"And that frightened you?"

"I was petrified. But not nearly as much then as I was later when I finally did learn the truth."

"And when was that?" Blake was curious in the way of all lovers.

Cindy smiled. "At the party."

"But afterward you—"

"I was afraid."

Blake's hands roamed upward. "You put me through hell!"

"I put myself through hell too."

Cindy tiptoed up to kiss his slightly rough chin and let her lips smooth over his skin playfully until he could stand it no longer and greedily directed their mouths to meet.

As Blake strained her to him, she was aware of her power over him. But it equaled out. He had the same amount of power to stir her.

"Make me a promise, Cindy," Blake appealed when at last he was able to drag his mouth away from her willing lips.

"What?" Cindy was breathless. The way she felt right then she would promise him anything!

"Tell me you'll marry me."

Such sweet words! "I'll marry you. Whenever, wherever . . . I'll marry you in a bus, on a train, jumping out of an airplane."

Blake laughed a little unsteadily.

"How about in a church?"

"That too!" Cindy felt marvelous!

Blake scooped her up off the ground, swinging her knees easily over his arm, and began to dance around the room. They twirled about until Cindy was afraid he was going to drop her. If he wasn't dizzy, she certainly was!

They were both laughing when Blake finally stopped and allowed her feet to regain the floor. Then a spark of returning unease replaced his laughter and caused him to prompt seriously, "You haven't told me yet, Cindy."

Cindy frowned at his sudden change. "What? I don't understand." Her frown deepened until at last she understood. It was so simple and yet so important.

"I've already told you in the best way I know how," she replied, her eyes momentarily becoming shadowed as she tried to explain. "I haven't had the best of luck with the men who've come into my life, and learning to trust one again is a lot for me, Blake."

His arms tightened as he whispered huskily, "I won't ever make you regret it."

Cindy smiled tenderly, allowing her eyes to fondly caress the handsome, chiseled features, the chestnut hair that curled slightly, the loving expression in his cinnamon-shaded eyes. "I love you, Blake," she said softly. "I'll always love you. You've become my life."

Blake gazed down at her. "You were my life from the first moment I saw you."

Cindy marveled at the winds of fate. If she hadn't been working for Mr. Sawyer that week, if Blake had waited until Monday to pay his call . . . She dropped her head onto his chest, hearing the strong rapid thumping of the heart that had come to mean so much to her.

"I'm glad you were persistent, Blake."

He chuckled. "Ronnie would call it just plain obstinate."

"Whatever. If you hadn't been . . ."

Blake threaded his long fingers into the fine strands of her dark hair and pressed her head closer against him.

"I thought I had really blown it when you left."

Cindy heard the suffering behind his words.

"Would you have come looking for me if I hadn't come back?"

Blake's hand forced her head upward. "What do you think?"

Cindy opened her mouth to give her opinion but was prevented from doing so by the hungry urgency of Blake's lips taking her own in such passionate perfection that she soon forgot what she had been preparing to say.

All that mattered was him—the warm hard feel of him which her body, curving naturally into his, knew in intimate detail.

Throughout her life Cindy felt as if she had been searching, and now that she had found what she had been looking for, she wasn't about to let her prize dissolve for want of nourishment. She would give everything she had, all she possessed! Her heart was brimming over with her love for him!

As the kiss deepened and the fever of his desire began to build, a corresponding heat exploded in her veins. And when his hands began to move over her, running familiarly over her feminine curves, it unleashed a torrent of reactions that caused her senses to spin giddily out of control. She pressed herself still closer against him, making him aware of her need and arousing him even more.

When Blake's fingers rose in compelling demand to the zipper of her thin dress, Cindy waited impatiently to be released from confinement. And when the warmth of his hands, slightly unsteady from the depth of his emotion, trailed along the skin of her back, she trembled as well.

Blake's mouth moved to her cheek before sliding on to the side of her neck. He murmured her name, his husky voice slurred.

Cindy ran her hands over the strong muscles of his shoulders then helped him slide the material of her dress lower to expose the twin mounds he had never disparaged. She arched so that he might kiss them.

As his lips touched the sensitive skin, Cindy let her head drop back in exquisite pleasure, her fingers tangling in the thickness of his chestnut hair.

Soon nothing would satisfy either of them except total union. Her dress ended up in a small heap on the floor and Blake's clothing quickly followed.

Cindy caressed his chest with her lips as he carried her to the couch.

When he placed her gently on its soft surface, Cindy met his heated gaze. What she saw was a reflection of what she felt: wonder, desire, and most of all, a tremendous love.

Then her vision was blocked by his head as he lowered his body onto hers. . . .

Increasing waves of passionate longing rose up to wash over them, drowning them to all but the delicious sensations of their own need, making them oblivious to time and place and to the dog who was now conveniently sound asleep a short distance away across the room.

It didn't matter in the least to Cindy that Blake had succeeded in everything he had set out to accomplish from the very beginning. It didn't matter because in the end, she had found that what he wanted was exactly what she wanted too! Her only problem had been that it had taken her a great deal longer than Blake to discover it!

LOOK FOR NEXT MONTH'S CANDLELIGHT ECSTASY ROMANCES™

"THE MOST ROMANTIC NOVEL SINCE LOVE STORY."
—Good Housekeeping
Change of Heart
SALLY MANDEL
Once in a long while, a story is so bursting with tenderness that its charm is irresistible.
That story is Sharlie and Brian's story, Change of Heart— a love story for a lifetime.
A Dell Book $2.95 (11355-5)